CONTEMPORARY GEOGRAPHY:
RESEARCH TRENDS

B. C. GEOGRAPHICAL SERIES, NUMBER 16

OCCASIONAL PAPERS IN GEOGRAPHY

edited by

ROGER LEIGH Ph. D.

Department of Geography
The University of British Columbia

Tantalus Research Limited

Publisher - Vancouver, Canada

B. C. GEOGRAPHICAL SERIES, NUMBER 16

Occasional papers in Geography
Canadian Association of Geographers
Western Division

Editorial Address:
W.G. Hardwick, Ph.D.
Department of Geography
University of British Columbia
Vancouver 8, B.C.

Circulation Address:
B.C. Geographical Series
P.O. Box 4248
Vancouver 9, B.C., Canada

S.B.N.   0919478-22-0

The Occasional Papers in Geography are designed
to facilitate circulation of papers and contributions
which may merit distribution from time to time.

PRINTED IN CANADA

TABLE OF CONTENTS

PAGE

iii

INTRODUCTION

Roger Leigh
University of British Columbia

The articles in this volume are based on papers presented at the annual meeting of the Western Division of the Canadian Association of Geographers, held in Vancouver, B. C. in March 1971. This is the second volume to originate from the conference. The first volume (Contemporary Geography: Western Viewpoints) included papers of a philosophical nature, on methodological issues and on research topics in urban geography. In this volume are included papers on physical geography and various aspects of human geography.[1] Most of the papers are "research oriented;" they report the results of research efforts, or review areas in which research is needed; this is in contrast to the more reflective or speculative papers of the first volume. A strong regional flavour is apparent in the volume, since several papers take Western Canada as the focus of study. These include the papers on the hydrology and climate of B. C. by Slaymaker and Woo, and the useful pair of papers on the history of settlement in B. C. by Henderson and White. Unified by an interest in regional economic development are the papers by Barr, North and Lai; interesting here is the implicit contrast in political variables between the areas discussed, and the impact of politics on economic development.

The papers collected here show a great variety in topics, methods, scales of analysis and so on. This is not surprising given the wide theme of the conference (Contemporary Geography) and the actual plurality of interests in modern geography. Thus the papers in this volume include examples of simulation studies (Woo), scientific, theory controlled observational studies (Crowley), historical studies of population distribution (Henderson, White), regional studies aimed at description (Barr), or at theory qualification (Evenden); the previous volume also included behavioral studies (Rothwell, Claus), and statistical descriptive studies (Peuker and Rase). In short the volumes display well the variety of methods that geographers employ in their attempts to provide "orderly descriptions of the areal differentiation of the earths surface." The common regional focus of several of the papers gives a cumulative significance to the results -- enhanced understanding of the geography of Western Canada.

NOTES

1. The paper by Frank Cunningham was presented at a winter seminar of the Division, not at the annual meeting.

ACKNOWLEDGMENTS

I would like to thank Professors John Chapman (Department of Geography, University of British Columbia) and Brian Sagar (Department of Geography, Simon Fraser University) for their help in the selection and editing of the articles included in this volume.

RECENT FLUCTUATIONS IN THE MEAN
DISCHARGE OF THE FRASER RIVER

H. Olav Slaymaker
University of British Columbia

INTRODUCTION

Mean and total annual discharge data are relatively infrequently analysed over time. More commonly the flow duration curve[1] and the Rippl method of flow mass curve analysis[2] are used to evaluate any temporal fluctuations that may exist. Yevjevich and Jeng[3] have analysed non-homogeneous mean discharge data. The variability of mean annual discharge has been analysed by Hurst[4] and the use of queuing theory to regulate storage has been developed by Moran.[5]

PROBLEM

The mean daily discharge of the Fraser at Hope (1913-1969) is 96,200 cubic feet per second and the drainage area, until 1952, was 83,700 square miles (Figure 1). When the Kenney Dam was completed in 1952, the drainage area was reduced by 5,400 square miles. In spite of this reduction in effective drainage area, since 1952 the mean daily discharge of the Fraser at Hope has exceeded the long term average in all years except 1953 and 1956 (Figure 2) and the mean daily discharge for the period (1953-1969) has been 105,100 cubic feet per second as compared with 92,400 cubic feet per second for 1913-1952.

From Table 1 it is apparent that a net decrease in mean discharge of 1,700 cubic feet per second could have been anticipated over the period 1952-1969 so that the increase in recorded mean discharge from 92,400 to 105,100 probably corresponds to an actual increase from 92,400 to 106,800 cubic feet

3

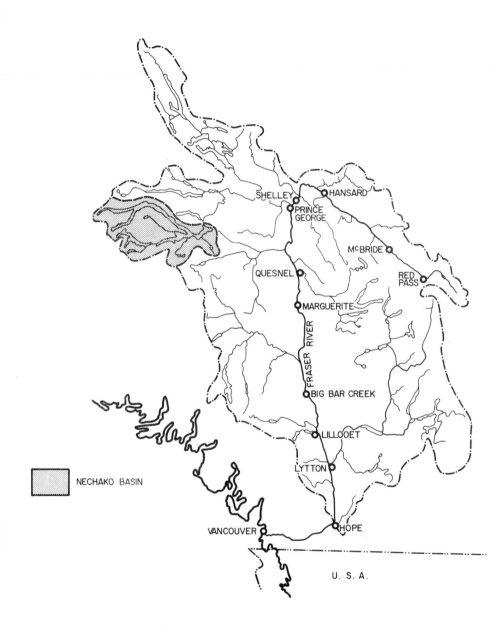

FIGURE 1 - FRASER RIVER DRAINAGE BASIN ABOVE HOPE

4

TABLE 1

Recorded and Adjusted Mean Discharge Data for the Fraser River at Six Stations

	Gauging Station	1953-57	1958-62	1963-67
A. Recorded Mean Discharge	Hope	98,300	107,400	108,600
	Texas Creek	59,800	67,000	70,300
	Big Bar Creek	53,500	61,900	64,100
	Marguerite	48,200	57,200	59,200
	Shelley	27,500	30,400	32,800
	Hansard	16,300	17,000	18,600
B. Adjusted Mean Discharge*	Hope	100,900	108,700	109,900
	Texas Creek	62,400	68,300	71,600
	Big Bar Creek	56,100	63,200	65,400
	Marguerite	50,800	58,500	60,500
	Shelley**	27,500	30,400	32,800
	Hansard**	16,300	17,000	18,600

*During 1953-57 the Nechako Reservoir was being filled. Recorded mean discharge was 2,600 cubic feet per second too low. During 1958-67, 2,200 cubic feet per second were diverted to the Kitimat-Kemano plant and 900 cubic feet per second were diverted into the Fraser system from the Nanika River.6 Recorded mean discharge was 1,300 cubic feet per second too low.

**Unaffected by Nechako Reservoir.

5

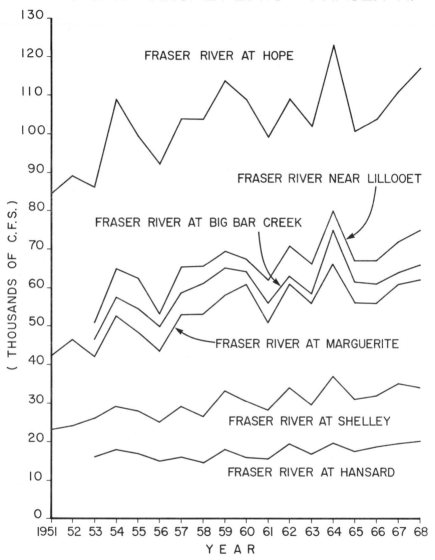

MEAN ANNUAL FLOWS – FRASER R.

FIGURE 2 - MEAN ANNUAL FLOWS AT SIX GAUGING STATIONS ON

FRASER RIVER (1953-1968)

6

per second. At the same time, preliminary analysis of precipitation data for 12 stations* in the Fraser River basin shows no upward trend that is statistically significant.

ANALYSIS

It was decided to try to isolate the region or regions responsible for the discharge increase by analysing the mean discharge data for successive primary gauging stations along the course of the Fraser River and subtracting mean values of discharge for the upper station from those of the lower station. Unfortunately, none of the stations upstream from Hope has whole year records from earlier than 1951. This means that detailed comparison is limited to the period 1952-1969, and only about 50 per cent of the discharge increase documented in the Hope record can be analysed.

Figure 3 shows the first areas examined: (a) between Hope and Texas Creek; (b) between Texas Creek and Big Bar Creek; and (c) between Big Bar Creek and Marguerite. Figure 2 and Table 1 confirm that there is no apparent increase in the mean discharge characteristics of these areas, as determined from the difference between successive gauging stations during 1953-67. These areas include the Thompson, the Bridge and the Chilcotin drainage.

Figure 4 shows the area between Marguerite and Shelley gauging stations, which includes the Nechako, the Stuart and the Quesnel basins. The mean discharges at Marguerite and at Shelley indicate that an increase of the order of 5,700 cubic feet per second can be attributed to this area. With all effects of diversion removed, about 4,400 cubic feet per second (or c.19 per cent) is the increase over 26,000 square miles (Table 1b).

_____

*Barkerville, Big Bar Creek, Fort St. James, Kamloops, Lillooet, McBride, Prince George, Quesnel, Red Pass Junction, Salmon Arm, Vanderhoof, Vavenby.

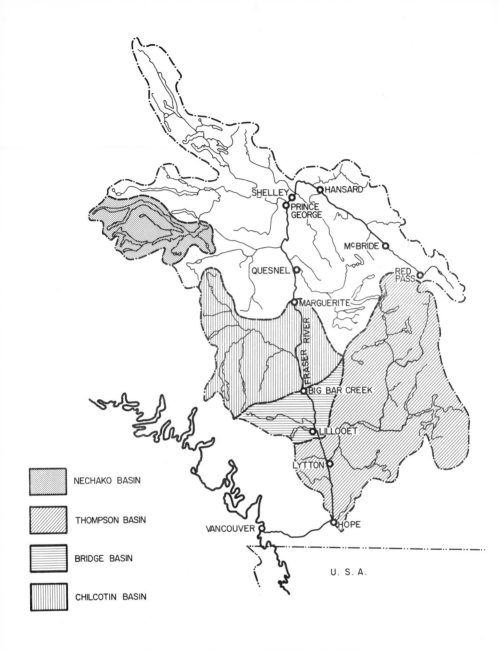

FIGURE 3 - FRASER RIVER DRAINAGE BASIN

    (a) BETWEEN HOPE AND TEXAS CREEK

    (b) BETWEEN TEXAS CREEK AND BIG BAR CREEK

    (c) BETWEEN BIG BAR CREEK AND MARGUERITE

8

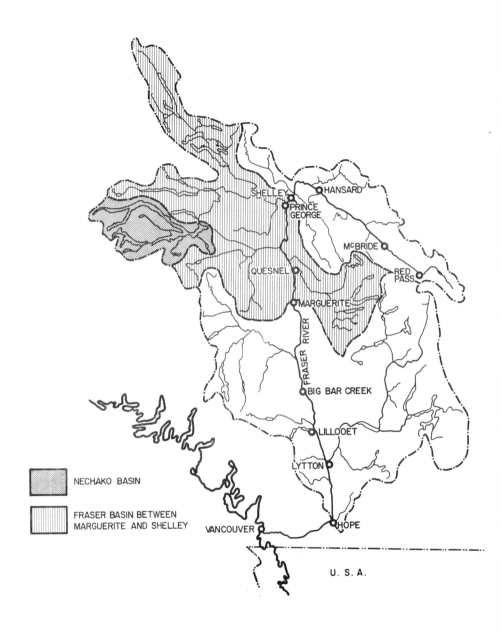

NECHAKO BASIN

FRASER BASIN BETWEEN
MARGUERITE AND SHELLEY

FIGURE 4 - FRASER RIVER DRAINAGE BASIN BETWEEN MARGUERITE

AND SHELLEY.

9

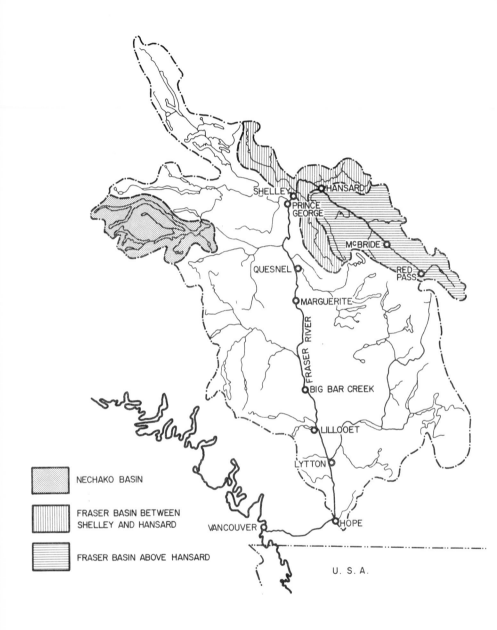

FIGURE 5 - FRASER RIVER DRAINAGE BASIN

        (a) BETWEEN SHELLEY AND HANSARD

        (b) ABOVE HANSARD

10

Figure 5 shows the area between Shelley and Hansard gauging stations and that above Hansard. In the former area an increase of 3,000 cubic feet per second (c.27 per cent) over 5,500 square miles has occurred and in the area above Hansard (7,000 square miles) an increase of 2,300 cubic feet per second (c.14 per cent) has occurred (Table 1a).

These are massive increases in mean discharge and, intuitively, such increases can only be accounted for by precipitation. Analysis of the Barkerville, Fort St. James, Prince George and Quesnel precipitation records in greater detail showed no significant upward trend as between 1953-57 and 1963-67.[7]

Analysis of the Hope record month by month as between 1913-50 and 1951-69 showed (by the Mann-Whitney U. test) that the mean annual discharge had significantly increased and that the October, November, December, January, February and March mean monthly discharges had significantly increased. The summer months showed no significant increase or decrease in discharge.

These recorded winter increases in discharge were primarily due to reservoir regulation on the Nechako system and much of the discharge released in winter is actually generated in summer. Two other factors possibly responsible for summer discharge increases are: (a) land use changes in the upper part of the Fraser basin; and (b) glacier melt contribution. Land use changes, important as they are in small basins, are not generally regarded as adequate to explain major changes in river behaviour over thousands of square miles. Glacier melt could well explain a portion of the increase. The glacier surveys of Alberta and British Columbia, show that ablation is occurring more rapidly in the Rocky Mountain area than in the Coast Mountains.[8] If one foot per year were ablated from the 150 square miles of glaciers and ice fields upstream from Hansard, the equivalent of 130 cubic feet per second would be added to the Fraser River mean discharge. This could then explain a part of the increased mean discharge in the Fraser River above Hansard. But for the adjacent regions of the basin there are no glaciers, and precipitation increase is the only possible explanation.

11

CONCLUSION

The unresolved problem is thus one of explaining an increase in the mean discharge of the upper Fraser basin of 19 per cent between 1953-57 and 1963-67. The only possible source is that of precipitation above the 3,000 foot level where there are no precipitation gauges. The meteorological factors producing such a local increase in high level precipitation during 1958-67 probably relate to the mean position of the Arctic front. The evidence given here suggests that the Arctic front must have occupied a more northerly mean position during 1958-67 than in 1953-57.

REFERENCES

1. Foster, H. A., "Duration curves," Transactions, American Society of Civil Engineers, 99 (1934), pp. 1213-1235.

2. Rippl, W., "The capacity of storage reservoirs for water supply," Proceedings, Institution of Civil Engineers, 71 (1883), pp. 270-278.

3. Yevjevich, Y. and R. I. Jeng, "Properties of non-homogeneous hydrologic series," Colorado State University, Hydrology Paper, 32 (1969).

4. Hurst, H. E., "A suggested statistical model of some time series which occur in nature," Nature, 180 (1957), pp. 494-495.

5. Moran, P. A. P., "A probability theory of dams and storage systems," Australian Journal of Applied Science, 5 (1954), pp. 116-124.

6. Wolcott, W. W., "Hydraulics of the Kemano development" in Alcan Nechako-Kemano-Kitimat Development, edited by The Engineering Institute of Canada (1955), pp. 3-5.

7. Jones, O. D., "Temperature and precipitation trends and variation of the Fraser River basin, B.C.," Graduating essay in Geography, U.B.C. (1953). See also, Wallis, J. H., "Precipitation in the Fraser River basin," M.A. thesis in Geography, U.B.C. (1963).

8. Campbell, P. I., I. A. Reid and J. Shastal, "Glacier survey in Alberta," Water Survey of Canada, Inland Waters Branch, Report Series No. 4, and also "Glacier surveys in British Columbia," Water Survey of Canada, Inland Waters Branch, Report Series No. 5.

COMPARATIVE EFFECTIVENESS OF THREE
STOCHASTIC MODELS OF PRECIPITATION

Ming-ko Woo
University of British Columbia

INTRODUCTION

Inherent in daily precipitation is the element of uncertainty which makes it desirable to handle the data through its probability structure. In other words, the occurrences of precipitation events and the magnitude of precipitation are stochastic processes. An understanding of the probability structure of daily precipitation enables an extension of short-term records through stochastic simulation to obtain statements regarding various long-term properties of precipitation. The purpose of the present study is to evaluate the relative merits of several stochastic models of precipitation.

THEORETICAL CONSIDERATIONS

The frequency, duration and magnitude of precipitation events are affected by atmospheric circulation patterns over the gauging site at which records are taken. Hence, persistence and intensity of different storm types should be taken into consideration when a mathematical model is developed. Various mathematical models have been formulated to examine the stochastic properties of precipitation at different time scales (Table 1). The present paper discusses only those approaches for handling the occurrences and durations of daily precipitation.

(1) Markov Chain Approach

A Markov chain is totally defined by its transition matrix and the initial distribution functions. In particular, a

TABLE 1

Summary of Selected References on Stochastic Properties of the
Occurrences of Wet and Dry Days

Author	Technique	Time Unit	Location
Feyerherm & Bark, 1967	Second-order Markov chain	Day	North-central U.S.A.
Gabriel & Neumann, 1957	First-order Markov chain	Day	Israel
Gabriel & Neumann, 1962	First-order Markov chain leading to geometric dist.	Day	Israel
Grace & Eagleson, 1967	Weibull distribution	Minute	Northeast U.S.A.
Green, 1964	Alternating wet and dry runs following renewal process	Day	Israel
Green, 1970	Modified Markov chain	Day	England
Hopkins & Robillard, 1964	Second-order Markov chain	Day	Canadian prairies
Longley, 1953	First-order Markov chain and cycles of geometric distribution	Day	Canada & U.K.
Sariahmed & Kisiel, 1968	Weibull distribution	Storm	SW U.S.A.
Simpson & Henry, 1966	First-order Markov chain	Day	Canadian prairies
Todorovic & Yevjevich, 1969	Poisson distribution for number of storms per period or day	Hour or day	Central U.S.A.

16

Markov chain with ergodic states will be aperiodic and has finite recurrence time.

With wet and dry periods, three assumptions are made:

i. The probability of a period being wet or dry is conditioned by the nature of the past period or a finite number of past periods. This assumption establishes the Markov property.

ii. The transition from a dry to a wet period (and vice versa) follows some probability which does not change with time except for the effect of seasonality. This assumption is made to satisfy stationarity in the weak sense.

iii. Neither wet nor dry periods will extend to infinite lengths. This and the above assumption establish the ergodic condition of the Markov chain.

From historical records, a transition matrix can be constructed by noting the frequencies at which a wet period is followed by a wet or dry period, and so on. The problem is how many past periods should be retraced before the effect of persistence can be ignored. Here, considerations regarding time base (hourly, daily, monthly, etc.) and physical climatology (convectional or frontal storms) play an important role. As basic time unit shortens, persistence effect becomes more pronounced and Markov chains of higher order may be required for a satisfactory model. Similarly, places where frontal activity predominates are likely to experience stronger persistence than areas where convection dominates.

(2) Probability Distribution Approach

The following Gabriel and Neumann,[4] wet or dry spells are defined on the basis of whether or not precipitation has been recorded on consecutive days. In many places (such as the area investigated below), the duration of spells is serially independent, meaning that they can be considered as independent random variables characterized by probability distributions.

To derive a theoretical distribution for wet spells, let λ be the probability mean rate of occurrence of wet spells. It will have the dimension of the reciprocal of time. Between time

17

t and time $t + \Delta t$, with Δt being a small increment of time, the probability for not experiencing the arrival of a wet spell is

$$P_O(t + \Delta t) = P_O(1 - \lambda_w \Delta t) \qquad (1)$$

where $P_O(t)$ denotes the probability of encountering no new wet spell at time t.

Re-arranging terms and letting Δt approach zero, we obtain the differential equation

$$\lim_{\Delta t \to O} \frac{P_O(t + \Delta t) - P_O(t)}{t} = P_O(t)$$

$$= -\lambda_w P_O(t) \qquad (2)$$

Since no event occurred at t=O, the initial condition will be $P_O(O) = 1$. Then, equation (2) will have the solution

$$P_O(t) = \exp(-\lambda_w t) \qquad (3)$$

If T is the elapse time to the arrival of a new spell, in terms of spell duration, such elapse time will constitute a set of independen random variables. Then, for some time $t < T$, the probability of not having any new cycle between time (O, t) will be

$$P_O(T > t) = P_O(t) = \exp(-\lambda_w t), \ t > O \quad (3.a)$$

Therefore, the elapse time to a new event will have the cumulative distribution function

$$F(t) = 1 - \exp(-\lambda_w t), \quad t > O \qquad (4)$$

with its density function

$$f(t) = F'(t) = \lambda_w \exp(-\lambda_w t) \qquad (5)$$

This shows that the time to the arrival of a new event (which is the same as the length of a spell), follows an exponential distribution.

Similarly, a distribution function $G(t)$ for the length of dry spells can be derived, with λ_d being the mean rate of occurrence:

$$g(t) = G'(t) = \lambda_d \exp(-\lambda_d t) \qquad (6)$$

Hence, like wet spells, the distribution of dry spells follows an exponential distribution.

<u>(3) Comparison of Several Models</u>

The Markov chain technique regards the occurrence of daily events as discrete units so that the probability of obtaining a sequence of n units before encountering an event of a different nature is

$$P_n = p^{n-1}a \qquad (7)$$

where $\qquad P_n$ is probability of having n consecutive units of one type

p is probability of incrementing the sequence by one unit. This is a conditional probability in the present study.

$q = (1 - p)$

The sequences follow a geometric distribution whose equivalent in the case with continuous time parameter is the exponential distribution.[6] This provides a theoretical linkage between the Markov chain and probability distribution approaches. One problem is knowing whether or not the discrete-time approach is superior to the continuous-time approach. Another problem is deciding on the order of the Markov chain required to characterize precipitation events for a particular region. An indirect way of solving these problems is to compare empirically the historical records with data generated by different stochastic models. Hence, the following section will evaluate the merits of:

(a) an exponential distribution model for wet and dry spells,

(b) a first-order Markov chain model, and

(c) a second-order Markov chain model.

TABLE 2

INPUT STATISTICS FOR THREE PRECIPITATION SIMULATION MODELS

STAVE FALLS

	OCT-DEC			JAN-MAR			APR-JUN			JUL-SEP		
MEAN WET SPELL LENGTHS (DAYS)	4.88			4.39			3.23			2.66		
MEAN DRY SPELL LENGTHS (DAYS)	2.47			2.92			3.56			5.20		
	O	N	D	J	F	M	A	M	J	J	A	S
P(WIW)	.7266	.8000	.8289	.7957	.7812	.7628	.7183	.6885	.6714	.6024	.6296	.6544
P(WID)	.3606	.3953	.4340	.3326	.3464	.3524	.3478	.2644	.2741	.1464	.1818	.2307
P(WIWW)	.7341	.8019	.8270	.8013	.7876	.7671	.7166	.6634	.6770	.5340	.6178	.6297
P(WIWD)	.7079	.7927	.8375	.7718	.7590	.7486	.7225	.7459	.6592	.7059	.6494	.6994
P(WIDW)	.4427	.4695	.5443	.3846	.4497	.4261	.3938	.3098	.3405	.2029	.2313	.2616
P(WIDD)	.3181	.3477	.3521	.3042	.2911	.3133	.3231	.2475	.2484	.1360	.1716	.2214
MEAN DAILY PREC. (MM)	14.0	12.3	13.3	13.9	12.3	10.5	8.6	8.2	7.7	7.4	7.4	10.9

UBC ADMIN

	OCT-DEC			JAN-MAR			APR-JUN			JUL-SEP		
MEAN WET SPELL LENGTHS (DAYS)	5.28			4.69			3.08			2.73		
MEAN DRY SPELL LENGTHS (DAYS)	2.54			2.94			3.78			5.45		
	O	N	D	J	F	M	A	M	J	J	A	S
P(WIW)	.7435	.8199	.8566	.8108	.7874	.7717	.7105	.6686	.6079	.6185	.6617	.6497
P(WID)	.3626	.4322	.3636	.3894	.3750	.2772	.3950	.2500	.2574	.1093	.1815	.2318
P(WIWW)	.7529	.8455	.8492	.7915	.8020	.7633	.6894	.6750	.6022	.5645	.6047	.6535
P(WIWD)	.7167	.7115	.9024	.8958	.7308	.8000	.7612	.6545	.6167	.7143	.7660	.6429
P(WIDW)	.4068	.5098	.3415	.5600	.4717	.3725	.4127	.2667	.3065	.1892	.2326	.3148
P(WIDD)	.3393	.3731	.3768	.2840	.3133	.2406	.3838	.2440	.2400	.0977	.1718	.2067
MEAN DAILY PREC. (MM)												

Higher-order Markov chain models are not included because of substantially increased modelling complexity and because of the want of physical verification of a long-term persistence effect.

STIMULATION OF DAILY PRECIPITATION

Daily records of precipitation for 1928-69 at Stave Falls, B.C., a coastal valley station, were used as a basis for the simulation experiments performed. Statistics pertinent to the three models were abstracted from the record (presented as Tabel 2), with most parameters taken on a monthly basis because of seasonal differences. For spell studies, however, seasonal values are used because spell lengths (especially dry spells) may exceed the length of a month. All three models assume that the amount of daily precipitation for any simulated wet day is exponentially distributed. This assumption has been substantiated by an excellent fit with historical data.[7]

One hundred years of precipitation data were simulated with each of the three approaches.[8] The beginning of a water-year is taken to be 1st October and a simulated water-year consists of 365 days (leap years are ignored). Figure 1 is a sample computer output simulated with wet and dry spells.

Several long-term properties of the simulated sequences and of the historical records were compared so that statements regarding the relative merits of different approaches could be made.

STATISTICAL COMPARISONS OF RESULTS

Several statistical tests were made to compare the quantity and duration of simulated precipitation events with those of historical data.

(1) Test for Spell Durations

The frequency distributions of wet and dry spells of various durations were abstracted from the data, and a two-sample Kolmogorov-Smirnov test applied to each pair of data sets. The results (Table 3) show that a second-order Markov chain reproduces

SIMULATED PRECIPIATION PLOT, DAYS 1 TO 122

+ SIMULATED VALUE
* POINT BEYOND MARGIN

P(mm)

135

90

45

0

DAYS SINCE 1st OCTOBER

Two-sample Kolomogorov-Smirnov Tests on

the Distribution of Spell Lengths

1. **D-statistics for dry spells**

	M.C.-1				M.C.-2				Exp. dist.			
	I	II	III	IV	I	II	III	IV	I	II	III	IV
M.C.-2	.076**	.081**	.036**	.034								
Exp. dist.	.084**	.072**	.088**	.046	.138**	.115**	.087**	.055				
Stave Falls	.078	.101**	.058	.036	.019	.066	.050	.029	.140**	.135**	.125**	.062
No. of samples	1272	1216	1335	1132	1250	1197	1329	1040	1087	1098	1133	1138

No. of samples for Stave Falls: I 507; II 501; III 562; IV 464

2. **D-statistics for wet spells**

	M.C.-1				M.C.-2				Exp. dist.			
	I	II	III	IV	I	II	III	IV	I	II	III	IV
M.C.-2	.017	.024	.015*	.027*								
Exp. dist.	.074**	.041	.065*	.064*	.066*	.046	.066*	.078**				
Stave Falls	.035	.022	.050	.047	.031	.027	.065	.020	.093**	.056	.105**	.076
No. of samples	1303	1205	1324	1123	1279	1194	1304	1137	1118	1087	1130	1024

No. of samples for Stave Falls: I 525; II 494; III 551; IV 464

Seasons   I   Oct.-Dec.
            II Jan.-Mar.
            III Apr.-June
            IV Jul.-Sept.

** D-statistics significant
   at 0.01 level
* D-statistics significant
   at 0.05 level

23

successfully the spell durations for all four seasons. The first-order Markov chain model is satisfactory in replicating wet spells but fails to produce a sufficient number of short dry spells during the wet seasons. The exponential distribution model is the weakest because the number of spells of short duration is often much smaller than that of historical data. This is attributed to the truncation of data simulated by a continuous distribution into discrete units of days (for instance, a simulated 0.6 day spell is considered as a one day spell).

(2) Tests for Annual and Monthly Precipitations

The quantity of annual precipitation is a useful comparison. Table 4 lists the means and variances computed from the four sets of data. A non-parametric Mann-Whitney U-test shows that their means are insignificantly different. On the other hand, variances of simulated data are considerably lower than that of historical data. This may be illustrated by plotting the recurrence time of annual precipitations of various magnitudes (Figure 2). All simulated annual precipitations of short return periods tend to be higher than historical data, while annual precipitations with return periods greater than five years tend to fall short of historical records. Hence, none of the models is capable of recapitulating the range of extreme events.

Applying the Mann-Whitney test to monthly periods similarly shows no significant differences between historical data and mean monthly precipitations generated by various models except for November values generated by exponential distribution. In this particular case, most of the monthly precipitations of various return periods fall below those of historical data. Graphically, historical data appears to yield a larger range of monthly precipitation, especially for the wetter months of December, January and February (Figure 3). When the sample distributions of generated and historical monthly precipitations were compared, however, a two-sample Kolmogorov-Smirnov test did not recognize significant differences at an 0.05 probability level.

Reduced to the time scale of individual spells, the probabilities of obtaining a certain amount of precipitation during

24

Table 4

Comparison of Annual and Monthly Precipitation

	ANNUAL	OCT	NOV	DEC	JAN	FEB	MAR	APR	MAY	JUN	JUL	AUG	SEP
Stave Falls Historical Data (41 Years)													
Mean	2098.	245.	244.	294.	262.	232.	188.	148.	113.	108.	60.	73.	130.
Variance	130175.	7803.	11512.	9928.	18830.	9686.	5253.	2739.	2976.	3117.	1796.	3053.	5911.
Exp. Dist. Simulated Data (100 Years)													
Mean	2056.	253.	246.	269.	246.	222.	177.	135.	119.	114.	79.	80.	117.
Variance	40373.	6604.	8059.	6531.	7070.	5245.	4673.	3217.	3115.	2187.	1739.	1761.	3166.
First Order M.C. Simulated Data (100 Years)													
Mean	2113.	258.	249.	294.	259.	237.	186.	143.	114.	105.	62.	76.	130.
Variance	43781.	4843.	5636.	7525.	8252.	5662.	4166.	2074.	2362.	1683.	1520.	1704.	3694.
Second Order M.C. Simulated Data (100 Years)													
Mean	2111.	247.	270.	295.	252.	235.	181.	144.	117.	108.	61.	71.	129.
Variance	48043.	6705.	6663.	6048.	6144.	6501.	4540.	1792.	2280.	1805.	1126.	1495.	5062.

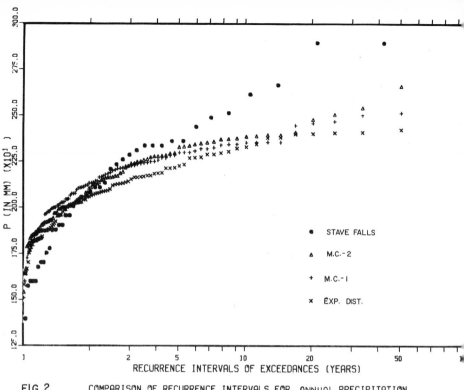

FIG. 2   COMPARISON OF RECURRENCE INTERVALS FOR ANNUAL PRECIPITATION

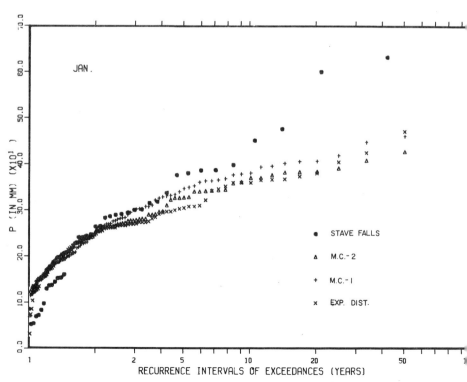

FIG. 3   COMPARISON OF RECURRENCE INTERVALS FOR MONTHLY PRECIPITATION

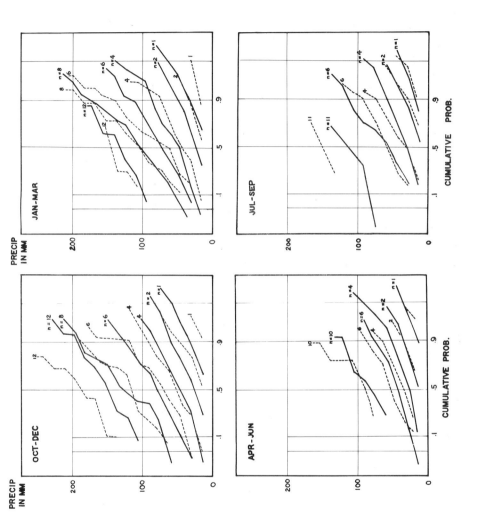

FIG. 4. Probability that an n-day spell has precipitation
exceeding a given quantity. (Full line is based on
data simulated with second-order Markov chain
model, dash line is based on data from Stave Falls.)

a spell of a certain duration were plotted for comparison. From the plots (Figure 4), it appears more likely that simulated data would produce higher precipitation than historical records. For wet spells of more than ten day duration, however, historical records are likely to produce higher precipitation. Such discrepancies between historical and simulated data arise out of the fact that simulated daily precipitation is less spread out towards the extremely low or high values (Table 5). Despite observable differences between the probability distributions of historical and simulated data, a two-sample Kolmogorov-Smirnov test shows that such differences are statistically insignificant.

DISCUSSION AND APPLICATIONS

Of the three models, the second-order Markov chain model has been able to replicate the occurrences of wet and dry spells most satisfactorily. While all models are capable of reproducing average conditions in annual and monthly precipitation, none of them has produced extreme events comparable to available records (Figure 5).

Bearing this limitation in mind, we may extend precipitation records of some other coastal mountain stations with one of the models presented. The second-order Markov chain model was selected to extend the records of University of British Columbia Research Forest station which has thirteen years of precipitation data. With a hundred years of simulated data, it is possible to eliminate phenomena such as 'outliers'[9] and long-term probablistic statements regarding spell durations or recurrence intervals of precipitation (Figure 6 and Figure 7) could be made with greater confidence.

ACKNOWLEDGMENTS

I am indebted to Dr. H. O. Slaymaker for his advice and useful comments, and to Dr. G. R. Gates who read and criticized the manuscript.

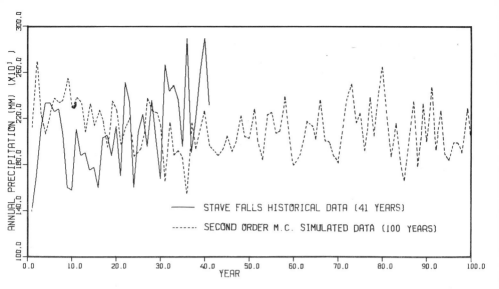

FIG. 5   COMPARISON OF HISTORICAL AND SIMULATED ANNUAL PRECIPITATION

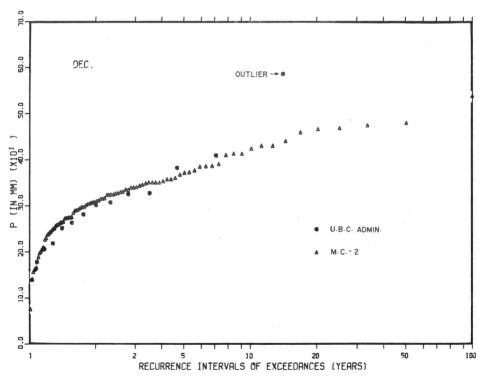

FIG. 6   COMPARISON OF RECURRENCE INTERVALS FOR MONTHLY PRECIPITATION

TABLE 5

Distribution of Daily Precipitation

Precip. class (in mm)	Cumulative Probability Distribution			
	Stave Falls	M.C.-1	M.C.-2	Exp.dist.
0.25	.368	.310	.312	.313
0.50	.548	.525	.522	.526
0.75	.674	.666	.663	.668
1.00	.762	.764	.761	.767
1.25	.829	.832	.830	.835
1.50	.878	.880	.877	.882
1.75	.912	.915	.913	.915
2.00	.932	.937	.937	.939
2.25	.949	.953	.954	.957
2.50	.961	.966	.966	.969
2.75	.971	.975	.975	.976
3.00	.977	.981	.981	.983
3.25	.982	.985	.986	.988
3.50	.987	.989	.990	.991
3.75	.989	.992	.993	.993
4.00	.992	.994	.995	.995
4.25	.994	.996	.996	.996
4.50	.995	.997	.997	.997
4.75	.996	.998	.998	.998
5.00	.997	.998	.999	.999
5.25	.997	.999	.999	.999
5.50	.998	.999	.999	.999
No. of samples	7796	18813	18731	18509

REFERENCES

1. Feyerherm, A. M. and Bark, L. D., "Goodness of fit of a
   Markov chain model for sequences of wet and dry
   days," Journal of Applied Meteorology, V. 6 (1967),
   pp. 770-773.
   Gabriel, K. R. and Neumann, J., "On a distribution
   of weather cycles by length," Quarterly Journal of
   Royal Meteorological Society, V. 83, (1957), pp. 375-
   380.

_____. "A Markov chain model for daily rainfall occurrence at Tel Aviv," Quarterly Journal of Royal Meteorological Society, V. 99 (1962), pp. 90-95.

Grace, R. A. and Eagleson, P. S., "A model for generating synthetic sequences of short-time-interval rainfall depths," Proceedings, International Hydrology Symposium, Colorado State University, Fort Collins, (1967), pp. 268-276.

Green, J. R., 'A model for rainfall occurrences," Journal of Royal Statistical Society, "Ser. B, V. 26 (1964), pp. 345-353.

_____. "A generalised probability model for sequences of wet and dry days," Monthly Weather Review, V. 98 (1970), pp. 238-241.

Hopkins, J. W. and Robillard, P., 'Some statistics of daily rainfall occurrence for the Canadian prairie provinces," Journal of Applied Meteorology, V. 3 (1964), pp. 600-602.

Longley, R. W., "The length of dry and wet periods," Quarterly Journal of Royal Meteorological Society, V. 79 (1953), pp. 520-527.

Sariahmed, A. and Kisiel, C. C., "Synthesis of sequences of summer thunderstorms volumes for the Atterbury watershed in the Tucson area," Intern. Ass. Sc. Hydrol., Pub. 81 (1968), pp. 439-447.

Simpson, W. and Henry, C. D., "Dry and wet spells at Winnipeg," Dept. of Transport Met. Br., Cir. 4507 (1966), 15 p.

Todorovic, P. and Yevjevich, V., "Stochastic process of precipitation," Colorado State University Hydrological Paper 35 (1969), 61 p.

2. Feller, William, Probability Theory and its Applications, V. 1, (New York: Wiley, 1968), p. 393.

3. Ibid., p. 420.

4. Gabriel and Neumann, 1957, Op. Cit.

5. Ibid., p. 375.

6. Feller, op. cit., p. 458.

7. To arrive at the exponential distribution theoretically, consider
   the following:

   > Since the time when a rain gauge is read (at a daily
   > interval) does not coincide with the duration of storms,
   > the amount of daily precipitation recorded can be
   > assumed to be serially independent. Then, let
   > $(\lambda_p)^{-1}$ be the mean quantity of precipitation collected
   > when the gauge is read. Between the points when the
   > gauge has collected x and x+ Δx units of precipitation
   > (Δx being a small increment of precipitation) the
   > probability of not taking a gauge reading is

   $$P_O(x + \Delta x) = P_O(1 - \lambda_p \Delta x)$$

   > where $P_O(x)$ is the probability that the gauge was
   > not read when it had collected up to x units of
   > precipitation.

   > This is similar to equation (1). Solving for it, we
   > obtain the exponential distribution for daily precipitation

   > It is interesting to note that the sum of exponentially
   > distributed random variables has a gamma distribution
   > which should be the consequent distribution for total
   > precipitation of a wet spell (defined as a continuous
   > sequence of one or more wet days). This coincides
   > with the findings of Todorovic and Yevjevich, op. cit.

8. Simulation and subsequent statistical computations were
   performed at the University of British Columbia
   Computing Centre with IBM/360 Model 67.

9. "An outlier in a series of extremes may be defined as an
   extremely rare event which disrupts the pattern
   established by the other observations." Hershfield,
   D. M. "An empirical comparison of the predictive
   value of three extreme value procedures," Journal of
   Geophysical Research, V. 67 (1962), p. 1541.

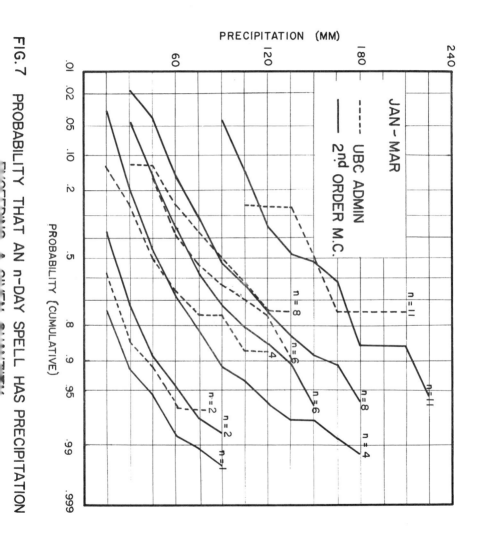

FIG. 7 PROBABILITY THAT AN n-DAY SPELL HAS PRECIPITATION

PALEOCLIMATIC SIGNIFICANCE OF ALLUVIAL FAN DEPOSITS IN THE SANGRE DE CRISTO MOUNTAINS, COLORADO

J. P. Crowley
University of Calgary

INTRODUCTION

Few alluvial fans in the arid regions of the western United States are actively aggrading and causes for this have been the subject of several investigations in recent years, such as the works of Lustig[1] and Melton.[2] Changes in the depositional characteristics of alluvial fans have been noted by both of the above investigators, the changes being linked to climatic variation during the late Quaternary. But despite the assertions of both writers, much of the difficulty in linking alluvial fan sedimentation to climatic change has been a lack of detailed analysis of alluvial fan sediments. This is understandable in numerous investigations, as most areas in which alluvial fans have their best topographic expression are found on igneous and/or metamorphic country rock which is not easily identified in the field without substantial petrographic work. However, in this study, the author undertook a study of alluvial fan sediments derived from drainage basins developed on sedimentary material of sufficiently varying lithology to allow identification of the material in the alluvial fan and to determine the sources within the drainage basin.

THE STUDY AREA

The Sangre de Cristo Mountains are a portion of the Southern Rocky Mountain Province as described by Fenneman[3] and trend north-south from near Salida, Colorado (38° 32' N. Lat., 106 02' W. Long.) to Santa Fe, New Mexico (35° 40' N. Lat.,

106°00' W. Long.). The range is bounded on the west by the San Luis Valley, a large intermontane basin some thirty to fifty miles in width. Alluvial fans are well developed and coalesce to form a sloping bajada surface between the floor of the San Luis Valley and the base of the Sangre de Cristo Mountains. Alluvial fan and bajada surfaces cover a 500 to 700 foot vertical section between the base of the San Luis Valley (7,500 feet above sea level) and the base of the Sangre de Cristo escarpment. The crest of the range varies from just under 10,000 feet above sea level to over 14,300 above sea level at Blanca Peak (37°38' N. Lat., 105°33' W. Long. The range has several 14,000 foot peaks within it and these form a very prominent sawtooth barrier to the east of the San Luis Valley.

PREVIOUS INVESTIGATIONS

Siebenthal[4] recognized several periods of glaciation in the Sangre de Cristo Mountains. In his investigation of the ground water geology of the San Luis Valley, he called attention to an apparent association of alluvial fan sedimentation and periods of glaciation, suggesting that they were perhaps contemporaneous although he did not concern himself further with the problem. Today, there are no glaciers, glacierets or large permanent snowfields either documented or evident from aerial photographs of the range. A basal tree line is found along the base of the range composed mainly of pinion pine. Higher in the range, douglas fir, aspen and spruce comprise the remaining major tree varieties.

Preliminary investigation by this writer in 1965 and 1966 indicated that two striking contrasts existed between the alluvial fans along the front of the range and the streams within the parent drainage basin. First, material comprising the alluvia fans was substantially larger than the modern bedload transported by the streams under present conditions and second, that the material comprising the modern bedload did not appear to be of the same lithology as the alluvial fan sediments. If the association between alluvial fan sedimentation and climate is ever to be successfully linked, it will be necessary to carefully demonstrate that climatic change should bring about concomitant changes in the sedimentary pattern of the alluvial fan.

Melton[5] showed that certain consistencies of alluvial

fan morphology could by linked generally to regional climatic conditions at the time of fan construction. Most notable of Melt on's hypotheses is an association of colder climates and higher sediment yield accounting for a once aggrading state on alluvial fans in southeastern Arizona rather than the association of widespread degradation under present climatic conditions.

Therefore, Siebenthal's earlier comments on the assocation of glaciation and fan construction are again worth noting in the study area. Clearly there is an association between glaciation and periods of high sediment yield. Corbel,[6] for example, has suggested that there is a fourfold increase in sediment yield over non-glaciated conditions, although this figure may be rather speculative. However, it is unlikely that glaciation is the direct cause of fan construction along the glanks of the Sangre de Cristo Mountains for numerous drainage basins were not glaciated either having elevations below cirque development or due to exposure. Much of the Sangre de Cristo Range is double-crested and the most prominent glacial features are found leeward of the first crest, suggesting that exposure was very critical at the time of glaciation.

REGIONAL GEOLOGY

Geologically, the Northern Sangre de Cristo Mountains (lying between Blanca Peak and Salida, Colorado) are a Precambrian-cored, Paleozoic sedimentary complex. Structurally, the range is highly folded and faulted. Despite this, a definite north-south strike of structure is readily evident from aerial photographs and previous mapping. Litsey[7] has to date supplied the most highly detailed mapping of any portion of the range. Figure 1 is a generalized geological column of the range.

LIME CANYON

Lime Canyon is a small drainage basin lying about mid-way between Blanca Peak and Salida, Colorado. It is a non-glaciated drainage basin and lies immediately north of Black Canyon which has experienced several periods of glaciation. Lime Canyon drains towards the southwest and has no topographic obstacles which might have permitted substantial snow accumulation

AGE	FORMATION	THICK-NESS	DESCRIPTION
CENOZOIC			GLACIAL GRAVEL AND ALLUVIUM
PENN. § PERM.	Sangre de Cristo	6,500'	Arkosic conglomerate interbedded with red micaceous sandstone and thin limestones.
PENN. § PERM.	Minturn	8,000'	Drab sandstones and fine conglomerates interbedded. Basal member is red micaceous sandstone.
PENN.	Kerber	0 - 150'	Sandstone and coaly shale.
MISS.	Leadville Limestone	230 - 340'	Limestone, massive, medium grey. Contains black chert nodules.
DEV.	Chafee Dyer	100'	Dolomite, finegrained to lithographic.
	Parting	50'	Quartzite and sandy shale.
ORD.	Fremont	240'	Dolomite, massive, medium grey fossiliferous.
	Harding Sandstone	65 - 116'	Quartzite, shaly zone at base.
	Manitou	120 - 200'	Dolomite, crystalline, weathers medium light grey or yellowish grey. Chert layers common.
PRECAMBRIAN			Hornblende gneiss and quartz biotite gneiss intruded by granite.

FIGURE 1

GEOLOGIC COLUMN FOR NORTHERN SANGRE DE CRISTO MOUNTAINS

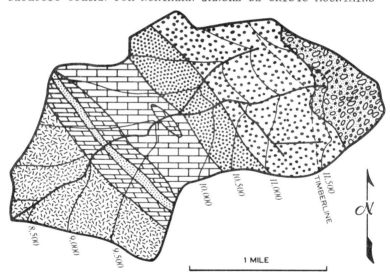

FIGURE 2

GEOLOGIC MAP OF LIME CANYON, SANGRE DE CRISTO MOUNTAINS

as may be the case where a double crest is present as in the adjoining Black Canyon. Lithologically, Lime Canyon is not complicated and three major lithologic types may be delimited, namely Precambrian crystallines and metamorphics, Lower Paleozoic carbonates and Upper Paleozoic clastics. Two units shown in Figure 1 are not exposed in Lime Canyon, namely the Kerber Formation and the Sangre de Cristo Formation. Aside from the two units mentioned, the geologic column in Figure 1 is representative of Lime Canyon. Figure 2 is a generalized geologic map of Lime Canyon. The Precambrian and Lower Paleozoic sequences are complete as described in Figure 1 and the clastic sequence is composed entirely of the Minturn Formation, a unit which may be subdivided into three distinct members. The lower member of the Minturn Formation is a distinctly red micaceous sandstone, the middle member a coarse sandstone which grades into the upper member, a coarse conglomerate. There is a high angle thrust faulting present in the lower regions of the basin which cause the Lower Paleozoic units (carbonates) to repeat several times. Faulting and strike and dip measurements have been deleted for simplicity in reading. Faulting and folding is attributable to Laramide orogeny althoug the range has doubtless experienced some post-Laramide tectonic activity.

SAMPLING

Sampling a feature as large as an alluvial fan is at best difficult, as the population is immense in sheer numbers of individual components and obtaining a representative sample may always be in question. This problem has been recognized and dealt with elsewhere by Wolman[8] who has suggested a systematic form of "grab-sampling." Basically, that sampling procedure was used by the writer.

Materials comprising the Sangre de Cristo alluvial fans are extremely coarse, with silt, sand and pebble fractions notably absent. An absence of fines was noted as well by Miller[9] in his work in the late 1950's in the southern portion of the Sangre de Cristo Mountains.

In sampling an alluvial fan, a key question is: what will most likely reveal the cause of the cessation of fan aggradation?

As the surface material represents the last deposition on the fan surface proper, it is felt that this should represent the area of concentrated investigation. Actual exposures through the Lime Canyon alluvial fan are limited to two, an abandoned railroad cut and the present stream course along the lateral edge of the fan. Nowhere is there an exposure greater than ten feet in depth. However, no variation in lithology of the gravels was noted in these comparatively limited sections. It is proposed that the surface was representative of lithologies through at least the first ten feet on this fan. Although the remarks above are directed toward the Lime Canyon fan, the assumptions made here are consistent with several other fans in the area. No changes in composition, soil profiles or other possible indicators of a hiatus were seen. Throughout the area, fans are composed of extremely coarse materials ranging from cobble to boulder-size materials. All deposits appear to be water-laid, poorly sorted and rather typical of torrential flooding. Mudflow activity was not in evidence on any fan surface.

Two sampling traverses were made along paths twenty degrees either side of the central axis of the fan. Samples were taken at one-hundred yard intervals and twenty rocks nearest that point were measured, described and assigned to the major litho-logic groups. Bedload sampling took place in a similar manner, taking twenty rocks across the bed of the stream at one-hundred yard intervals upstream from the fan apex. In all, some 640 samples were taken from Lime Canyon fan and 340 from Lime Canyon stream. The percentage of each major lithologic type is shown in Table 1. The clear difference[10] between both populations in size and in lithologic characteristics would indicate that the source area of the fan material is not the same as the source of the present bedload. The dominant lithology in the present bedload is derived from a source area approximately two thousand feet above the source of the dominant lithology in the fan surface.

The dominant lithologies in the modern bedload are derived from the higher reaches of the drainage basin near or above the present timberline. Figure 2 has the topographic con-figuration and the timberline indicated. The observation might not be unexpected as Rapp[11] has shown that mechanical processes are most abundant within the first few hundred feet above the timberline

40

TABLE 1

Lime Canyon

Fan Surface Unit		Bedload Unit	
1. Precambrian	20%	1. Precambrian	8%
2. Harding	2%	2. Harding	2%
3. Dolomites	11%	3. Dolomites	3%
4. Limestone	61%	4. Limestone	16%
5. Basal Minturn	3%	5. Basal Minturn	10%
6. Middle Minturn	1%	6. Middle Minturn	29%
7. Upper Minturn	1%	7. Upper Minturn	26%
Unidentified	5%	Unidentified	4%

Mean Size 4.1"   Means Size 2.3"
Sample Size 680   Sample Size 340

Inasmuch as no topographic or depositional evidence is present that would suggest that Lime Canyon was glaciated, then some change in the level of mechanical processes must have occurred. Since Lime Canyon fan is a torrential stream deposit, mechanical agents must have been more active in the 9,000 to 9,500 foot level of the basin in order to have yielded the substantially higher percentage of carbonate material than is present in the modern channel.

EVIDENCE OF CLIMATIC CHANGE

Certainly the above comments might infer a change in mechanical processes within the drainage basin. However, numerous ancient talus slopes are present below the timberline and these slopes have stabilized. Vegetation is well established on the slopes, the material shows a definite weathering surface and the slope angles (24-27°) fall well within Melton's[12] criteria of slope stability. Slope angles on talus material above the tree line approach repose angle and the author has measured year to year movement on such slopes. Mechanical agents have been or are now present throughout the Lime Canyon basin. Stagnant talus slopes are found in the 9,000 to 9,500 foot level composed of the carbonate materials found on the fan surface.

Glacial History

Six major and minor glaciations have been recognized in the southern Rocky Mountains in the past 25,000 years. Table 2 shows the chronology for the southern Rocky Mountains during the late Quaternary.

Immediately to the south of Lime Canyon is a glaciated drainage basin, Black Canyon, in which late Quaternary moraines are present as well as three distinct rock glacier advances. A buried till with no topographic expression is overlain by three more recent advances which are assignable to Pinedale glaciation on the basis of their altitudinal position. Table 3 gives the elevation of end moraines in the Sangre de Cristo Mountains. The elevation of moraines in this area corresponds quite closely in elevation to those documented by Richmond[13] in the Colorado Front Range, some one hundred miles to the northeast. The older till in Black Canyon is assigned to the Late Bull Lake stade, and has the lowest exposure (9,000 feet above sea level) in that basin.

Pinedale moraines, particularly the lateral moraines are in varying states of preservation as valleyside wastage has tended to obliterate particularly the Pinedale I moraines. Talus activity as well has removed or buried portions of the Pinedale II moraines, whereas the Pinedale III remain largely intact with only limited burial or removal above the timberline.

Basing the periods of climatic depression on strati-graphic evidence, the last period of mass wastage below the presen timberline would have closely corresponded to the Pinedale III stade. Therefore, a date of Pinedale III is suggested for the period of last major aggradation on the Lime Canyon fan as well as other fans throughout the local area. Neoglaciation is responsible for rock glacier activity in many portions of the Sangre de Cristo Mountains and three apparent advances are present in Black Canyon.

CONCLUSIONS

Surficial evidence suggests that several glacial or periglacial environments have been present within the study area

42

TABLE 2

GLACIAL CHRONOLOGY OF THE SANGRE DE CRISTO MOUNTAINS

	PERIOD	APPROX. AGE (Years B.P.)
NEOGLACIATION	Gennett Peak Stade Interstade Arikaree Stade Interstade Temple Lake Stade	100 350 950 1,850 2,650 4,500
ALTITHERMAL INTERVAL		4,500-7,500
PINEDALE GLACIATION	Late State (III) Interstade Middle Stade (II) Interstade Early Stade (I)	10,000 12,000 25,000
INTERGLACIATION		25,000-32,000
BULL LAKE GLACIATION	Late Stade Interstade Early Stade	

TABLE 3

ELEVATION OF END MORAINES (MSL)
SANGRE DE CRISTO MOUNTAINS, COLORADO

NEOGLACIATION	Gannett Peak Stade Arikaree Stade Temple Lake Stade	Cirque Glaciation Cirque Glaciation Cirque Glaciation
PINEDALE GLACIATION	Late Stade (III) Middle Stade (II) Early Stade (I)	10,800-11,000 10,000-10,300 9,900-10,200
BULL LAKE GLACIATION	Late Stade Early Stade	8,900-9,300 Below 8,700

and that associated with these periods have been marked increases in slope wastage and hence basin sediment yield. Furthermore, the areas of mass wastage during the Pinedale stades also correspond to areas of high stream energy within drainage basins. It is quite possible that this is reflected in the larger sized material comprising the Lime Canyon alluvial fan, although jointing and fracture patterns may also be in part responsible.

It is proposed that the climatic depression experienced in the range during the Pinedale III period resulted in an increased sediment yield which permitted the existence of an aggrading environment at that time. Conditions favourable to high sediment yield and transportation are not present under the climatic regime of today. Thus it appears that cessation of fan construction likely occurred between the climatic minimum of Pinedale III and the postulated Altithermal in the southern Rocky Mountains.

Timberline must have been depressed from 2,000 to 2,300 feet below the present level during the period of last active fan construction. If present lapse rates for the Rocky Mountains (7.5°F/1,000') are extrapolated for Pinedale events,[15] this would represent a cooling of mean July temperature from 15-17°F.

At a given time in its history, an alluvial fan is representative of hydrologic conditions which result either in its aggradation, degradation or possible stability. Further studies of source area, particle size, coupled with theoretical considerations of stream morphology, and tractive force, may allow a highly reliable estimation of hydrologic conditions during late Quarternary events -- climatic proxies which are badly needed.

44

REFERENCES

1. Lustig, L. K., "Clastic sedimentation in Deep Springs Valley, California," U.S. Geological Survey Professional Paper, 352-F, (1965), pp. 131-192.

2. Melton, M. A., "The geomorphic and paleoclimatic significance of alluvial deposits in Southern Arizona," Journal of Geology, Vol. 73, (1965), pp. 1-38.

3. Fenneman, Physiography of Western United States, (New York: McGraw-Hill, 1931), pp. 92-110.

4. Siebenthal, C. E., "Geology and water resources of the San Luis Valley, Colorado," U. S. Geological Survey Water Supply Paper 240, (1910), p. 128.

5. Melton, op. cit.

6. Corbel, J., "Vitesse de l'erosion," Zeits. für Geomorphologie, Vol. 3, (1959), pp. 1-28.

7. Litsey, L. R., "Stratigraphy and structure of the Northern Sangre de Cristo Mountains, Colorado," Bulletin Geological Society of America, (1958), pp. 1143-1178.

8. Wolman, M. G., "A method of sampling coarse river-bed material," American Geophysical Union Translations, Vol. 35, (1954) pp. 951-956.

9. Miller, J. P., "High mountain streams, effects of geology on channel characteristics and bed material," New Mexico State Bureau of Mines and Mineral Resources, Memoir 4, (1958), pp. 51.

10. Differences are statistically significant. The Kruskal-Wallis one way analysis of variance was used on differences between fan and bedload materials and the "z" test was used on size differences.

11. Rapp, Anders, "Recent development of mountain slopes in Karkevagge and surroundings," Geografiska Annaler, Vol. 42, (1960), 185 pp.

12. Melton, M. A., "Debris-covered hillslopes of the southern Arizona desert-consideration of their stability and sediment contribution," Journal of Geology, Vol. 73, (1965), pp, 715, 729.

13. Richmond, G. M., "Glaciation of the Rocky Mountains," in Wright, H. E., Jr. and Frey, D. G. (eds.), The Quaternary of the United States, (Princeton: Princeton University Press, 1965), pp. 217-230.

14. Benedict, J. B., "Downslope soil movement in a Colorado alpine region: rates, processes, and climatic significance," Arctic and Alpine Research, Vol. 2, (1970), pp. 165-226.

15. Galloway, R. W. "The full-glacial climate in the southwestern United States," Annals, Association of American Geographers, Vol. 60, (1970), pp. 245-256.

THE PRESENT STATE OF GEOMORPHOLOGICAL
RESEARCH ABOUT LATIN AMERICA

Frank F. Cunningham
Simon Fraser University

Because of Latin America's great size and complexity, the shortage of geographical research about it compared to that about North America or Europe, and the dispersal of effort between scholars from the many Latin American countries and from outside countries, it is difficult for any single person to undertake a review of any field of geographical enquiry focussing on Latin America. Nevertheless this paper attempts such a review; it first surveys the state of research in physical geography about Latin America, and then discusses in more detail the record and prospects in terms of the geomorphological study of Latin America. The paper is followed by a list of references of recent works on the geomorphology of the region; due to space limitations, the list is highly selective; a more comprehensive bibliography is available from the author.

The most important incontestable fact is that while the importance of Latin America is paid constant lip service, the amount of geographical (and other) research is woefully inadequate. Latin Americans are multiplying faster than are the people of any other major area in the world; there are already more Americans south of the Rio Grande del Norte than north of it, and by the year 2,000 A.D. there will be twice as many if present trends continue. How Latin Americans develop their countries in the next 20 years, and which other co-operating nations earn their esteem in this process are among the most vital world issues. It is in this context that the following characteristics of geographical research about Latin America should be seen:-

    i) it is quite insufficient in amount;

    ii) the locales studies are scattered almost indiscriminately over the area;

  iii) the research has been done by a relatively large number of investigators or, to put it less favourably, few people have done much by way of concentrated research;

  iv) the topics undertaken are multifarious, generally unco-ordinated, often palpably derived from lines of enquiry which originated in Europe or North America, and when set against the urgent problems of the area their objectives are frequently inconsequential;

    v) the contributions of foreign scholars are disproportionately significant, and consequently a sound acquaintance with the research literature demands a competence in many languages;

  vi) these disadvantages have collectively deferred the relative comprehensiveness of data which governments, planners, contractors, agronomists, and new researchers, (to say nothing of educators) so urgently require.

A significant though partial proof of these contentions was provided by the 1970 National Conference of Latin American Geographers, held at Ball State University, Muncie, Indiana where 8⁰ geographical specialists led by the redoubtable Preston James and representing the largest single pool of Latin Americanists in the world, met to review where research in each systematic branch of geography stood, as far as its pursuit in Latin America was concerned, in order that a program for the 70's could be the better formulated. Without exception each specialist presenting a paper deplored the insufficiency of research done in his particular branch.[1] It is further noteworthy that, in addition to this general complaint, the papers were divided into two main groups, the second of which was dubbed 'Neglected Fields.' In the list of 'Neglected Fields' number one was Physical Geography!

Geographers conventionally make a quite indefensible subdivision of reality whereby 'physical' includes not merely rocks and rivers but also plants and animals, but this arrangement of material only strengthens the present argument. At the Muncie Conference, Charles Bennet (University of California at Los

48

Angeles) regretted both how little zoogeography had been done in Latin America (shades of Darwin and Bates!) and the rarity of zoogeographers being trained in U.S.A.

Philip Wagner, (Simon Fraser University, British Columbia) was more trenchant about research during the '60's into Latin America's vegetation -- "it is all too easy to summarise the decades work: it has been sparse." He lamented the "vast lack of first-hand knowledge," and criticized the pre-occupation of so many U.S. vegetation geographers with the problem (still unresolved) of the origin of savanalands.

All physical geography studies about Latin America (not only those concerning animals and vegetation) are crippled by the paucity and lack of standardisation of climatic data, at both the macro-level (used by some climatologists) and the micro-level (important to land use). Outside of large towns and specialised sites (especially airfields) regularly observed data are exceedingly rare. Few of the existing meteorological stations meet the require-ments of the World Meteorological Office. Only one original source book for climatic data covering all of Latin America has ever been compiled (Koppen and Geiger -- 'Handbook of Climatology'), and though no single fact in it is later than 1927 it is perforce quoted ad nauseam in geography texts. Apart from over the Caribbean, atmospheric circulation (knowledge of which is vital in weather forecasting, air travel and crop production) has not been properly investigated. If the proposed Global Atmospheric Research Program is ever implemented (whereby satellites will provide simultaneous observations every hour for a whole year) there will be few areas where so much revaluation of basic ideas will result as in Latin America.

Of the several sub-branches of physical geography, this account is particularly concerned with geomorphology. There is most certainly a shortage of North American geomorphologists interested in Latin America. For example in 1970 the P.A.I.G.H. made a survey of the special interests of over 100 Canadian Latin Americanists and found that of them only three confessed to geomorphological interests. Contributors to the Muncie Conference, already mentioned, emphasised this shortage in various ways. The biogeographers there complained of the lack of geomorphological data, especially of those concerning slope changes resulting from agricultural practices in tropical conditions. Dieter Brunnschweiler (Michigan State University) suggested that, because in his opinion Latin American higher education was not geared to producing earth scientists, U. S. Universities should undertake such training for 1,000 Latin Americans per year. The disparity between, on the one hand this ambitious proposal, and present realities on the other, was illustrated by Craig's[2] contention that if called on to supply for each Latin American country but one geomorphologist who already had some expertise in that country's geomorphology, the U.S.A. could not do it!

It has to be remembered, however, that research by United Statesers or even North Americans by no means encompasses all the geomorphological work involved. The decrease of geographical research by North Americans with increasing distance from the United States has been remarked on. Even in Middle America, the local scholars and Europeans are prominent, and in South America their work predominates.

The range, limitations and other characteristics of geomorphological research about Latin America are nowhere better exemplified than from a perusal of 'Geomorphological Abstracts,' the most comprehensive record available of research articles throughout the world in the last decade.[3] For 1960 the appropriate volume included 225 abstracts of which only 5 concerned Latin America i.e. 1 in 45. For 1970, when just over 2,000 articles were abstracted, over 100 concerned Latin America i.e. 1 in 20, so according to this measure Latin American interest has expanded disproportionately with the undoubted increase of geomorphological publications in the '60's. Scrutiny of the subjects reveals, however, that the same limiting characteristics noted earlier as being typical of physical geography enquiry as a whole are also true for geomorphology. For instance studies have been very localised, there is a marked paucity of studies which cover the whole of Latin America, or more than one country there, or even of work applying to the whole of any one country.

The specific topics which have attracted most scholars to date also clearly reveal the immature stage of research about Latin America. Such topics far more often seek to meet an intellectual challenge than to solve one of Latin America's innumerable real problems. Works such as Maria Novaes Pinto's on natural and man-made erosion in the favelas of Rio de Janeiro, or Humberto Espinal's study of the costs (in terms of personal injury, property damage and financial waste) which have resulted in Venezuela from urban expansion without prior research of sub-surface conditions, are only too rare. The remarkable shortage of hydrological studies for an area which includes some of the greatest river systems in the world, where agriculture occupies half the workers, where the fantastic scrabble to urbanise is crippled by the lack of safe water, and where water so widely constitutes the only cheap power potential, has often been pointed out. This lack is the more unexpected in view of the marked and indeed, some would think, excessive pre-occupation of North American geomorphologists with 'process. '

What has actually been studied in Latin America? That coastal geomorphology has been relatively popular may be partly explained by the great stretches of coast available in Middle America (which is the easiest section for foreign scholars to reach), by the concentration of most of South America's population in coastal areas, and by the importance of overseas trade to Latin America's economy. In spite of this popularity, one of the most prominent scholars[4] involved could write in 1970 "the lack of precise data at the most elementary level is appalling." Apart from the enterprising work emanating from the University of California at Berkeley, from Louisiana State University (where Richard J. Russell has been a key figure), and from the University of Cambridge (England), little of this coastal enquiry has been long-term or has involved groups of investigators.

A good deal has been done about beach geomorphology, especially in the Caribbean and in Barbados in particular, for example by MacIntyre. Characteristically, much of this research has been directed at former beach and coral levels with implications for Pleistocene climatic and isostatic fluctuations. This emphasis on what is essentially historical methodology has not displeased archaeologists, who can benefit from the datings or sequences provided. Archaeologists also have a particular interest in coastal studies of Peru and North Chile. One of the most fascinating of these is that by J. A. Broggie who has advanced the idea that the dunes along the arid Peruvian coastal fringe are only wind-driven

51

when below the persistent cloud layer which is so typical there. He has proceeded to attempt correlation between fossil dunes of different ages (which are now within the cloud layer) with earlier climatic fluctuations.

In fact as far as Latin American geomorphology is concerned nearly all roads lead (backwards) to the Pleistocene. Of course Pleistocene addicts have a very tempting field in Latin America. Existing glaciers occur at intervals throughout the length of the Andes (with small ones in Mexico), and traces of former glaciation are very extensive. The Patagonian Andes have attracted the most concentrated enquiries about existing glaciers and Colqui has reviewed this field, although important subsequent work has been done, e.g. by Flint. The Argentinian Government has sponsored some of the most important work. There is a great deal of scattered information about Andean glaciers gleaned by numbers of mountaineering expedicitions (A. Olszewski has attempted to co-ordinate this information), but a uniform Pleisto-cene chronology has proved elusive. The search for four glacial advances a la Penck and Bruckner, not surprisingly, was gratified in some places. In others only three have been proved. In Argentinian Patagonia there are ample traces of two such glaciation (Magnani's study in 1962) but in Northern Colombia only of one. Of course such evidence may in fact be only the lack of evidence. The fact that five glacials have been proved in the Alps and in Alaska is a further complication.

The search for Pleistocene chronologies has been pursued not only in the glaciated areas and, as has been noted, along former shore lines, but also from sea-bed cores where the work of Emiliani on Caribbean evidence is probably the best known. Investigation of fluctuations of the lakes of the Andean altiplano has begun, following lines similar to those used to unravel the change of Lakes Bonneville and Lahontan in the Great Basin, but with the added attraction that contemporary occupance in the altiplano included skilled cultivators who coped with complex altitudinal migrations of lake shore-lines and also agriculturally-significant temperature thresholds. Mario Magnani after studying Mexican glaciers has suggested that pluvial enquiry would be a more productive way to unravel Pleistocene changes there.

Latin American scholars, especially Brazilians, have been clearly influenced by post-Davisian developments in geomorphology and although many such developments stem from Walter Penck (who studied in the Andes for a time) the clearest ties exist between such work in Brazil and that of Lester King, the doyen of South African geomorphologists. King's recognition of ancient pediplanation levels has been followed up in eastern South America where as many as seven such levels (some correlated with African ones) have been suggested. Of many recent Brazilian geomorphologists, the work of Joao Jose Bigarella and his colleagues is especially noteworthy.

Latin America presents a uniquely favourable field for vulcanologists. As a single instance, in a study of volcanoes near Arequipa, Peru, Armin Hoempler writes of one valley which has 36 cones associated with four different periods of activity. But surprisingly this field has been little ploughed.

Certain limited areas of Latin America have been studied in relative detail because of circumstances additional to their intrinsic interest. This is particularly true of Puerto Rico with its special relationships with USA, and the Guianas with special relationships with Britain, the Netherlands and France. Of a considerable range of work emanating from U.S. scholars working in Puerto Rico, perhaps the most notable is that of John D. Weaver (especially about former planation surfaces in Middle America), and of H. Watson Monroe (particularly but by no means exclusively about karst geomorphology in Puerto Rico). In passing it should be observed that considerable karst work has also been done in Jamaica and Yucatan; some of this work is described in the 1969 Journal of the British Speleological Association.

British, Dutch, and particularly French scholars have contributed numerous studies of the Guianas. Many of these have concerned laterisation because this is important in agricultural development, in the origin of bauxite, and, as so often pursued in Latin America, in palaeoclimates. Much work has been done on coastal sedimentation and Jean Tricart's contribution to this would itself be significant, but is only one of many geomorphological aspects pursued widely over Latin America (and elsewhere) by this indefatigable French scientist.

A quite unusual interest has long been shown in Colombia's geography by German scholars, from the times of Alexander von Huboldt to the present, and this has included some significant geomorphological work (notably that of Hettner concernin, the Bogota region). The extent of German interest may be gauged from the fact that Uhlig has written a complete book about the contributions of Germans to Colombia geography.

It may be appropriate to conclude by emphasising that while almost all fields of geomorphology present unusual opportunities in Latin America, the most neglected are probably hydrology and structure. It will seem odd to North Americans that Horton's seminal work has had little impact in the Southern Americas. It is similarly a matter for astonishment that, except incidentally in the search for oil, our ideas of structural geology about Latin America are not being continuously revolutionised. It is significant that in 1968 the Hafner Publishing Company could turn out a new edition of Schuchert's classic "Historical Geology of the Antillean-Caribbean Region" which was an exact facsimile of the 1935 original. To fill those gaps there is a need for continued localised studies and doubtless these will go on, but there is a greater need for large-scale, long-term and necessarily expensive enquiry, undertaken by teams and institutes backed by national bodies. It is to be hoped that priority would be given to projects which have some foreseeable pay-off for the majority of Latin Americans.

REFERENCES

1. These papers are excellent summaries, and most have valuable references. The proceedings of the Muncie Conference are to be published shortly.

2. Alan K. Craig (Florida Atlantic University).

3. The editor and publisher, Professor Keith M. Clayton, has given permission for the inclusion of the 'Geomorphological Abstracts' reference number for the articles listed at the end of this account. 'Geomorphological Abstracts' are in such general use that there would be merit and convenience in using its reference numbers instead of authors and titles.

4. Norbert P. Psuty (Rutgers State University), who contributed two papers to the Muncie Conference, one on geomorphology in Middle America, the other on coastal morphology of Latin America.

BIBLIOGRAPHY OF SELECTED ARTICLES

Bigarella, J. J. "Palaogeographische und Palaoklimatische Aspekte des Kanozoikums in Sudbrasilien," Zeit. fur Geomoph., 8 (3), 1964, pp. 286-312. 65/213

_____. "Nota explicativa acompanhando a folha geologica de Paranagua, (Brazil) Boletim da Univ. do Parana, Geologia, 13, 1965, 6 pp. 67A/123

Bigarella, J. J. and De Andrade, G. O. 'Contribution to the study of the Brazilian Quarternary," Geological Soc. America, Special Papers 84, 1965, pp. 433-451. 66A/640

Bigarella, J. J. and Mousinho, M. R. "Significado paleogeografico e paleoclimatico dos depositos rudaceos." (S. Brazil) Boletim Paranaense de Geografia, 16 & 17, 1965, pp. 7-16. 1967A/38

_____. "Contribuicao ao estudo da Formacao Pariquera - Acu (Estado de Sao Paulo) Boletim Paranaense de Geografia, 16 & 17, 1965, pp. 17-41. 67A/179

_____. "Slope development in southeastern and southern Brazil, Zeit. fur Geomorph., 10 (2), 1966, pp. 150-159. 67A/577

Bigarella, J. J., Bousinho, M. R., and Da Silva, J. G. "Process and environments of the Brazilian Quaternary," Conselho de Pesquisas, Universidade do Parana, 1966, 71 pp. 67A/176

_____. "Pediplanos, pedimentos e seus depositos correlativos no Brasil," Boletim Paranaense de Geografia, 16 & 17, 1965, pp. 117-151. 67A/69

_____. "Consideracoes a respeito da evolucao das vertentes," Boletim Paranaense de Geografia, 16 & 17, 1965, pp. 85-116. 67A/70

Broggi, J. A. "Las ciclopeas dunas compuestas de la costa peruana, su origien significacion climatica," Boletin Sociedad Geol. del Peru, 36, 1961, pp. 61-66. 68A/247

Colqui, B. S. "Argentine glaciology," Antarctic Research, American Geophysical Union 1962, pp. 217-228. 63/479

_____. "Repertorio actualizado sobre informacion recogida en glaciares Argentinos," Acta Geologica Lilloana, 7, (1967), pp. 63-78. 68A/791

Emiliani, C. Paleotemperature analysis of the Caribbean Cores A254-BR-C and CP-28. Bull. Geol. Soc. America, 1964, 75 (2) pp. 129-144. 65/770

Espinal, V. H. "The importance of geological studies in construction projects," Boletin Informativo, Associacion Venezulana de Geologia Minera Petroleo, 8 (6)

1965, pp. 155-177. 68A/1261

Flint, R. F. and Fidalgo, F. "Glacial geology of the east flank
of the Argentine Andes between latitude 39° 10'S and
latitude 41° 20'S," Bull. Geol. Soc. America, 75 (4)
1964, pp. 335-352. 65/753

_____. "Geologia glacial de la zona de borde entre los paralelos
39° 10' y 41° 20' de latitud sur en la cordillera de los
Andes, Republica Argentina," Direccion Nacional de
Geologia y Mineria, Boletin 93, 1963, 35 pp. 67A/159

_____. "Glacial drift in the eastern Argentine Andes between
latitude 41 10'S and latitude 43 10'S." Geological
Society America, Bulletin, 80 (6), 1969, pp. 1043-
1052. 70A/891

Hoempler, A. L. O. "Valle de volcanoes de Andahua, Arequipa,"
Boletin Sociedad Geologica del Peru, 37, 1962, pp. 59-
59. 68A/15

Lehmann, H. "The classical Karst terminology in the critical light
of modern climatic morphology," (in French) (includes
Puerto Rico, Cuba and Jamaica) Revue de Geog. de
Lyon, 35 (i) 1960. 61/97

MacIntyre, L. G. "Submerged coral reefs, West Coast of
Barbados, West Indies," Canadian Journal Earth
Sciences, 4 (3), 1967, pp. 461-474. 68A/949

Magnani, M. "Indagini e richerche sulle glaciazioni e sulla
morfologia periglaciale in Argentina," Ricerca
Scientifica, 32 (2)Rend. Sez. A2 (4), 1962, pp. 297-
312. 68A/130

_____. "Uber MexiKanische Gletscher," Polarforschung 34 (5),
parts 1-2, 1965, 11. 275-278. 68A/190.

Monroe, W. H. "Evidence of subterranean sheet solution under
weathered detrital cover in Puerto Rico," Problems
of the Karst Penudation, (Brno), 1969, pp. 111-121.
70A/944

_____. "High-level Quaternary beach deposits in northwestern Puerto Rico," United States Geological Survey, Professional Paper, 600C, 1968, pp. C140-C143. 69A/18

_____. "The karst features of northern Puerto Rico," National Speleological Society, Bulletin, 30 (3), 1968, pp. 75-86. 70A/1308

_____. "The Zanjon, a solution feature of karst topography in Puerto Rico," U. S. Geol. Survey, Prof. Paper, 501-B, 1964, pp. B126-B129. 64/737

_____. "Sinkholes and towers in the karst area of north-central Puerto Rico," U. S. Geol. Survey, Professional Papers 400-B, 1960, p. 356. 62/435

Moody, C. L. "Gulf of Mexico distributive province," Bull. Amer. Ass. Petrol. Geologists, 51 (2), 1967, pp. 179-199. 68A/731

Olszewski, A. "Niektore problemy zlodowacen wspolczesnych i plejstocenkich Ameryki Poludniowej," Czasopismo Geograficzne, 38 (3), 1967, pp. 243-274. 68A/1850

Pinto, N. V. "A cidade do Rio de Janeiro: evolucao fisica e humana," Revista Brasileira de Geografia, 27 (2), 1965, pp. 191-232. 68A/1064

Psuty, N. P. "Regiones geomorficas tabasquenas," Union Geografica Internacional Conferencia Regional Latinoamericana, Tomo III, 1966, pp. 38-45.

_____. "Beach ridge development in Tabasco, Mexico," Annals Assoc. American Geographers, 55 (j), 1965, pp. 112-124. 66A/434

_____. "The geomorphology of beach ridges in Tabasco, Mexico," Coastal Studies Inst., Louisiana State Univ., Tech. Report 30, 1967, pp. 1-51. 68A/886

Psuty, N. P. and Bailey, J. S. "Lagoons, islands, off-shore

islands, shorelines and banks," Earth resource surveys from spacecraft, Vol. 2, ed. R. A. White, (Houston: N.A.S.A., Earth Resources Group), 1969, pp. G7-G14. 70A/1664

Russell, R. J. "Preliminary notes on Caribbean beach rock," Second Caribbean Geol. Conference, 1959, Trans. (1960), pp. 43-49. 62/419

_____. "Origin of beach rock," (Caribbean), Zeit. fur Geomorph. 6 (j), 1962, pp. 1-16. 63/126

Russell, R. J. and McIntyre, W. G. "Barbuda reconnaissance," Coastal Studies Series, Baton Rouge, Louisiana State University Press, 16, 1966, 53 pp. 67A/1537

Smith, D. I. (ed.) "Limestone Geomorphology: a study in Jamaica," Journal British Speleological Association, 6 (43/44) 1969, pp. 85-166. 70A/1309

Tricart, J. "Epandage hydrovolcanique quaternaire au pied du Volcan Baru, au bord du rio Escarrea"(Panama) Photo Interpretation 67-3 (3) 1967, pp. 15-21. 69A/412

_____. "Rapport entre le milieu physique et la geographie agraire" (Cours inferieur de rio La Villa, Se de Chitre, Panama). Photo Interpretation 67-3 (2) 1967, pp. 8-14. 69A/258

_____. "Delta lagunaire" (Rio Parita, Azuero), (Panama). Photo Interpretation 67-3 (1), 1967, pp. 1-7. 69A/411

_____. "Delta lagunaire de Rio Santa Maria, E. de el Rincon (Panama)," Photo Interpretation 67-2, 1967, pp. 36-42. 68A/1774

_____. "Formes littorales tropicales (extremite W. de l' J. Sevilla, Chiriqui, Panama," Photo Interpretation 67 (2) 1967, pp. 29-35. 68A/1897

_____. "Une plaine fluviomarine," (Panama) Photo Interpretati‹
67-2, 1967, pp. 22-28. 68A/1775

_____. "Accummulation deltaique," Photo Interpretation 67 (2)
1967, pp. 8-14. 68A/1895

_____. "Deltas Lagunaires, embouchere du Rio Santa Maria,
S.E. d' Aguadulce, Panama," Photo Interpretation
67 (2) 1967, pp. 1-7. 68A/1898

_____. "Geomorphologie et amenagement rural (exemple du
Venezuela)." Cooperation Technique, 44/45, 1966,
pp. 69-81. 67A/253

_____. "Aplicaciones de la geomorfologia en las obras de
ingenieria y especialmente en los estudios agrologicos,
Union Geografica Internacional Conferencia Regional
Latinoamericana, Tomo III, 1966, pp. 3-10.

_____. "Observations on the Quaternary firn line in Peru,"
Journal of Glaciology 5 (42), 1965, pp. 857-863.
66A/134

_____. "Apercu Sur le Quaternaire du Salvador (Amerique
centrale) Bull. Soc. Geol. de France 7 (3) 1961
63/43

Tricart, J. and Michel, M. Monographie et carte geomorphologiq‹
de la region de Lagunillas (Andes venezueliennes) Revu‹
de Geomorph. dynamique, 15 (J-3) 1965, pp. 1-33.
67A/392

Tricart, J. and Mainguet, M. Caracteristiques granulometriques
de quelques Sables eoliens du desert Peruvien, aspects
de la dynamique des barkanes," Revue de Geomorph.
dynamique, 15 (7-9), 1965, pp. 110-121. 67A/505

Tricart, J. and Hirsh, A. R. "Presentation de quelques essais de
cartes Geomorpholique detaillees realises au Centre
de Geographie Appliquee (Strasbourg)," (includes
Armacao, Brazil), Rev. Geomorph. dynamique, 14
(1-3), 1963, pp. 21-34. 65/559

Tricart, J. and Lillies-Lacroix, A. "Les terraces quaternaries des Andes venezueliennes," Bulletin Soc. Geologique de France, Ser. 7, 4 (2), 1962 (pub. 1963), pp. 201-218. 67A/1232

Tricart, J., et al. Note sur quelques aspects geomorphologiques de la Foret de Pierre de Huaron (Andes Centrales Peruviennes) Revue de Geomorph. dynamique, 13 (7-9), 1962, pp. 125-129. 64/344

Tricart, J. and Da Silva, T. C. "An example of Karst evolution in tropical dry conditions: the residual hill of Bom Jesus de Lapa, Bahia, Brazil," (in French) Zeit. fur Geom. 4 (J), 1960, pp. 29-42. 61/93

Uhlig, H. "Die Sierra Nevada de Santa Marta (Kolumbien)," Natur und Museum, 96 (2), 1966, pp. 50-59. 68A/447

Weaver, J. D. "Higher Level Erosion Surfaces in the Caribbean," Trans. 3rd Carib. Geol. Conf., Kingston, Jamaica: Jamaica Geol. Survey Bull., 95 (1966), pp. 10-12. 68A/121

_____. "Some remarks on the origin of the 'Nipe Clay' in Puerto Rico," Jamaica Geol. Surv. Pub., 95, 1966. 68A/122

_____. "The nature of the 'Nipe Clay' on Las Mesas, Western Puerto Rico," Zeit. fur Geomorph., 6 (2), 1962, pp. 218-232. 63/28

_____. "Notes on some erosional features in Virgin Gorda, Br. Virgin Is.," Caribbean Jour. Science, 2 (4), 1962, pp. 159-167. 63/532

_____. "Erosion surfaces in the Caribbean and their significance," Nature, 190 (4782), 1961, pp. 1186-1187. 62/154

_____. "Note on higher level erosion surfaces of Puerto Rico," Second Caribbean Geol. Conference, 1959, Trans., (1960), pp. 96-98. 62/364

RESEARCH IN HUMAN GEOGRAPHY

THE CHANGING SETTLEMENT PATTERN OF THE HAIDA

John R. Henderson
Washington State University

INTRODUCTION

European contact with the Haida Indians resulted in a complete reordering of the settlement pattern on the Queen Charlotte Islands, British Columbia. Liquor, diseases and new economic and cultural patterns contributed to the abandonment and consolidation of the Haida villages. What follows is an examination of the depopulation and migration pattern which emerged from the impingement of the products of Western culture on this group of native North Americans.

SETTLEMENT PATTERN CIRCA 1774

In 1774 when the Spanish explorer, Juan Perez, first viewed the mist-enshrouded Queen Charlotte Islands, he estimated that 9,800 people inhabited them. [1] These people, who we know collectively as the Haida, occupied 34 permanent villages scattered along the rocky coast of the islands. Each village belonged to a clan of either the Eagle or Raven moiety, and each constituted an autonomous political entity. All inhabitants of a settlement were members of the same clan and were governed by a clan headman. The clans of each moiety owned, in addition to their village site, portions of fishing streams and berry-picking territory to which they traveled during their yearly cycle. Mobility was a dominant characteristic of the Haida. In their ten fathom canoes, they ranged as far as Vancouver Island to trade or frequently to conduct raids against other tribes. Therefore, communications among the villages, via water transport, were indeed very good.

63

DISEASE AND DEPOPULATION

Following Perez's initial visit, the Spaniards sent another expedition to the North Pacific under the commands of Bruno Hecata and Bodega y Quadra. British explorers followed suit in 1786 with voyages of Portlock and Dixon. On a subsequent voyage the following year Dixon laid plans for a fur trading and processing center on the northern end of the Queen Charlottes. The target of the fur trade was the sea otter, and Dixon's first trading encounters proved fruitful. The Haida eagerly traded sea otter pelts for tin kettles, pewter basins, brass pins, buckles, and knives. Dixon's trading expedition in 1787 yielded a total of 2,552 pelts worth $54,867.[2]

Word of these high profits spread rapidly to England and the United States. Soon ships of all descriptions plied the waters around the Queen Charlotte Islands in search of furs. Pelts were bought at inflating prices; staple goods quickly superceded trinkets as the medium of exchange.

However, the fur trade brought more than wealth to the Haida. It also brought disease and liquor. Smallpox raced through the Queen Charlotte Islands in the 1780's, 90's and again in 1829. The Haida affixed the name "Tom Dyer" to the disease after the sailor who supposedly first brought smallpox to the Islands.[3] In 1860 and 1862 smallpox, carried from Victoria, swept through the villages on the Queen Charlottes, proving fatal for almost all who contracted it. Other "sicknesses of the white people," particularly measles and tuberculosis, plagued the Haida. English traders introduced liquor to the Haida in the late 1780's, as evidenced by an island traveler P. J. Cleveland who reported great quantities of cheap liquor in the native settlements in 1789.[4] Captain Vancouver, in 1794, noted the debilitating effects of rum on the native population.[5] Drunkenness weakened many and opened their bodies to infection from the prevalent diseases.

All these conditions, smallpox, measles, tuberculosis, drunkenness, combined to cause the population to decline from the estimated contact total of 9,800 to approximately 6,700 by 1840, a loss of over 30 per cent in about 65 years.[6] All regions of the Queen Charlotte Islands felt the effects of population decline.

However, two villages At'ana on House Island and Hagi on Bolkus Island were either completely wiped out or abandoned by 1836.[7] In many settlements, the population loss rendered them unviable.

Although population loss caused some population shifts in the 1840's and early 1850's, no strong attractive force of migration existed. From the late 1850's, through the 1870's, phenomena producing centripetal forces came to the Islands. The first such force was the exploitation of the Islands' mineral resources. The Hudson's Bay Company explored for and struck gold in 1851,[8] but the Bay's first extended mining expedition the following year proved disastrous, and gold fever subsided until 1859 when the Bay organized another expedition.[9] Although the sample assayed from this second search dashed hopes of a gold rush to the Queen Charlottes, the ore containing little gold, a ton of the rock held copper worth $72.00 and iron worth $135.00.[10] The Queen Charlotte Mining Company was organized to exploit the copper, but the vein soon played out. In order to recoup this loss on copper, the Queen Charlotte Mining Company extracted coal; however this operation too quickly succumbed, not for lack of coal, but for lack of transportation and a ready market.

The mining era lasted but a brief fifteen years, yet its impact on the Haida was far-reaching and permanent. Mining did not spur the economy of the Islands, but it brought Europeans to settle in close proximity to the Haida. Although these early mining settlements were small and ephemeral, they gave rise to grandiose plans of pioneers, railroads, roads, and cities. Through mining, the Islands and their native people became known to missionary societies who sent investigators to evaluate the opportunities for new mission fields, to speculators who sought land for mining and agriculture; and to traders who saw new customers for their wares. Even though fur traders had frequented the Islands for nearly ninety years, it was the fifteen years of mining which really opened the Islands to European settlement.

The Hudson's Bay Company controlled trade around the Queen Charlottes from their posts at Fort Simpson and Victoria. They, therefore, saw no need for a trading post on the Islands. That is, they saw no need until an American invaded their territory and built a post first at Cumshewa and then Masset in 1869. Upon

65

hearing of this Yankee incursion, Bay officials bought out the American trader and established a post themselves at Masset in 1871. This American was doubtless happy to sell, for the Masset Haida had just run him out of their village at the end of a gun. The year following the takeover of the Masset post, a Hudson's Bay Company ship began paying regular visits to Skidegate.[11]

THE MIGRATION PATTERN TO 1876

The trading posts at Masset and Skidegate created strong centripetal forces on the Queen Charlottes. With the exception of the Yaku-lennas to Yaku move and the Kiusta to Kung move, all village abandonment occurred in or after 1871. Figure 1 illustrates the migration pattern to 1876. Village names underscore with a solid line represents those villages which still existed in 1875. Those underscored with a broken line represent villages which received in-migration and later, they, themselves, were abandoned. The general pattern exhibits a west to east trend with a concentration near the sites of the trading posts, Masset and Skidegate. But these two villages themselves received only minor in-migration. Masset absorbed only the people of Yaku, and Skidegate received the inhabitants of Nai-koon, Lana-Inagai, and the Cape Ball group.

In 1875 the villages of Yatza, Yan, Masset, Skidegate, New Gold Harbour, Tsahl, Skedans, Tanu, a fraction of Ninstints, Dadens, Cumshewa, and Kayung remained.

MIGRATION PATTERN 1876-1897

The last great pulling force began in 1876 when the Church Missionary Society of London set a missionary to Masset. He brought white man's medicine to fight white man sickness; he brought schools to learn the white man's ways, and, incidentally to the Haida, he brought Christianity. By 1876 the native population had dwindled to approximately 2,000; smallpox, measles, venereal disease, and tuberculosis left them weak and desperate.[12] The missionary was warmly welcomed as a potential savior for the Haida. The people of Skidegate, hearing of the curing power of the missionary, asked that they too have such a person. In 1883 a lay minister from the Methodist mission school at Fort Simpson came

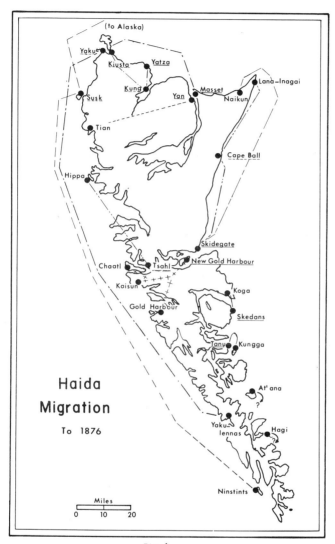

(to Alaska)

Yaku
Kiusta
Yatza
Kung
Susk
Yan
Masset
Naikun
Lana-Inagai
Tian
Cape Ball
Hippa
Skidegate
Chaatl
Tsahl
New Gold Harbour
Kaisun
Koga
Gold Harbour
Skedans
Tanu
Kungga
At'ana
?
Yaku
Iennas
Hagi
Ninstints

Haida

Migration

To 1876

Miles
0   10   20

Fig. 1

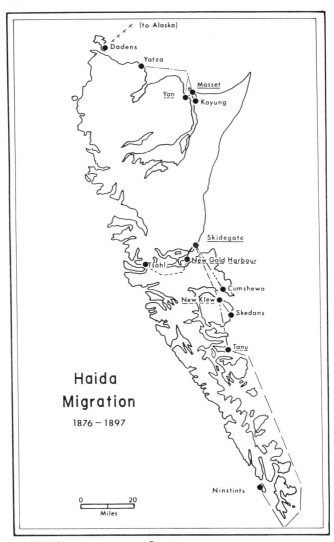

(to Alaska)

Dadens

Yatza

Masset

Yan

Kayung

Skidegate

New Gold Harbour

Tsahl

Cumshewa

New Klew

Skedans

Tanu

Haida
Migration

1876 – 1897

Ninstints

0   20

Miles

Fig. 2

to Skidegate and built a church.[13] Soon the village of Tanu asked
for a mission and a school, which they received after moving to a
more accessible location called New Klew. Prior to the move,
Tanu received the remnants of the Ninstints people, and after
moving the inhabitants of Skedans, migrated to New Klew. New
Gold Harbour requested and received a mission in 1885.[14]

By 1884 villagers of Yatza, Yan, and Kayung had
migrated to Masset, and by 1889 only Skidegate, New Klew, and
New Gold Harbour remained in the south. The total Haida population
had dwindled to 730 by 1889. Distribution of that population was as
follows:

Population of the Queen Charlotte Haida[15]
1889 - 1897

	1889	'90	'91	'92	'93	'94	'95	'96	'97
Masset	445	438	407	401	405	385	364	354	363
New Klew	93	94	93	84	77	73	58	66	*
Skidegate)									
New Gold Harbour)	192	198	193	197	192	*	*	*	*

In 1893 New Gold Harbour merged with Skidegate, and in
1897 the 66 remaining souls of New Klew moved to Skidegate. Of the
original 34 villages, Masset and Skidegate survived to the twentieth
century.

The same general migration pattern emerges, with the
addition of the centripetal forces added by the presence of the
missionaries. That is, a general movement of those farthest away
from the centers of gravity migrating first, but moving nearer, not
to, the actual centers.

ANALYSIS OF MIGRATION PATTERN

The migration pattern of the Haida on the Queen
Charlotte Islands proves opposite to that of Ravensteins first two
"Laws of Migration." These "Laws" state: 1) Migrants enumer-
ated in a certain center of absorption will. . . grow less as distance
from the center increases, and 2) inhabitants nearest the center
of attraction will first migrate followed by those from the margins

of the country.[16] Haida migration, conversely, began from points farthest away from the centers of attraction, and proceeded in a series of steps with each step moving closer to the center of attraction. For example, the Ninstints-Tanu-New Klew-Skidegate migration illustrates this stepping process. (Figure 2)

The pattern of migration can be explained by three phenomena: 1) The influence of the locations of trading and mission stations; 2) the traditional political autonomy of each village; and 3) efficient modes of native transportation. Selection of Masset and Skidegate by the traders and missionaries as the sites of their respective stations, of course, structured the overall migration pattern.

The stepped migration pattern resulted from the traditional political autonomy of each Haida village. To migrate directly to Masset or Skidegate meant surrendering the independence of their village. By minimizing the combination of villages, conflict was avoided.

And finally, the traditional mode of transportation, the ten fathom canoe, enhanced this stepped migration pattern. As noted earlier, the Haida were a mobile people, ranging as far as the southern end of Vancouver Island. Therefore, no village was isolated from European influences. Paddling distance to the trading post or mission was the major factor in village relocation. It was not necessary, therefore, to migrate to Masset for the desired services.

The combination of depopulation and the desire for European trade goods, medical services, and education, irreversibly altered the settlement pattern of the Haida Indians on the Queen Charlotte Islands.

REFERENCES

1. Kroeber, A. L., Cultural and Natural Areas of Native North America (Berkeley: University of California Publications in American Archaeology and Ethnology, Vol. 38, 1939), p. 115. For an account of Perez's voyage see De La Pena, Fray Tomas, "Diary of the Voyages of the Santiago, 1774," in Documents from the Sutro Collection (Los Angeles: Publications of the Historical Society of Southern California, 1891), pp. 83-143.

2. "Letter and Memorandum from Capt. George Dixon to Sir Josep Banks Regarding the Fur Trade on the Northwest Coast, A.D. 1789," The White Knight Chapbooks, Pacific Northwest Series, No. 3 (White Knight Press, March, 1941), n. p.

3. Green, J. S., Journal of a Tour on the North Coast of America in the Year 1829 (New York: Hartman's Historical Series, No. 10, 1915), p. 39.

4. Howay, F. W., "The Introduction of Intoxicating Liquor Amongst the Indians of the Northwest Coast," British Columbia Historical Review, 6 (1942), p. 163.

5. Ibid., p. 164.

6. This is the estimate of John Work found in Dawson, G. W., "Report on the Queen Charlotte Islands," Report of Progress for 1878-79 (Montreal: Geological Society of Canada, 1880), p. 173.

7. Hodge, F. W., Handbook of Indians of Canada (Ottawa: C. H. Parmelee, 1913), p. 48.

8. Copies or extracts of correspondence relative to the discovery of Gold at Queen Charlotte Island, 1853, (Victoria: Archives of British Columbia, unpublished).

9. Torrens, Capt. R. W., Report of Travels in Form of Letter Written to Gov. James Douglas, 29 December 1859,

71

(Victoria: Archives of British Columbia, unpublished handwritten), pp. 1-3.

10. Ibid., p. 5.

11. Daizell, K. E., The Queen Charlotte Island, 1774-1966 (Terrace, B.C.: C. M. Adam, 1968), p. 76.

12. Dawson, G. W. op.cit., p. 174.

13. Crosby, T., Up and Down the North Pacific Coast by Canoe and Mission Ship (Toronto: The Missionary Society of the Methodist Church, 1914), p. 265.

14. Ibid., p. 267; Scott, R. C., My Captain Oliver, A Story of Two Missionaries on the British Columbia Coast (Toronto: United Church of Canada, 1947), p. 27.

15. Department of Indian Affairs, Annual Report for 1889 (Ottawa: King's Printer 1890), p. 263; Annual Report for 1890, pp. 243-44; Annual Report for 1891, p. 244; Annual Report for 1892, p. 314; Annual Report for 1893, p. 309; Annual Report for 1894, p. 280; Annual Report for 1895, p. 359; Annual Report for 1896, p. 432; Annual Report for 1897, p. 85.

16. Ravenstein, E. G., "The Laws of Migration," Journal of the Royal Statistical Society, 48 (1885), p. 199.

THE MORPHOLOGY OF SETTLEMENT IN THE NOOTKA SOUND REGION OF VANCOUVER ISLAND'S WEST COAST 1900 - 1970

Brian P. White
Simon Fraser University

INTRODUCTION

During the first decades of the twentieth century, human occupance in the Nootka Sound Region has been characterized by a high degree of settlement mortality and settlement mobility. Since 1900 more than a score of European settlements have developed, prospered and have been eventually abandoned in an area studied by this writer, that is in the coastal area close to the waters of Nootka Sound and Nootka Island and in the drainage basins of rivers flowing into those waters.[1]

Three stages in the development of settlement patterns are suggested for the purposes of this study. The first stage comprises dispersed, small-scale and often mobile forms of settlement, typified by a high mortality (failure) rate. The acquisition of rights to timber, land, and minerals on a speculative basis is characteristic of the period which lasted from 1900-1920.

The second stage is defined by settlements based on more stable industries, with settlement typically located on the interface between land and sea. The rapid development of nucleated settlements based on resource extraction and processing, principally in the Esperanza Inlet and Zeballos Arm areas, provided the settlement focus in the area between 1920 and the commencement of the Second World War. Settlement mobility (float camps) remained a feature in the settlement morphology. Zeballos, the first town in the study area, developed as a result of a gold rush in 1936.

The third stage, covering the years 1940 - 1970, was initially characterized by a period of high settlement mortality between 1940 and 1952, due to changes in resource availability, extraction feasibility, and market demand. Canneries, pilchard reduction plants, and gold mining in Zeballos closed down, while logging and sawmilling accelerated in importance to become the principle source of employment in the region. Since 1952 the consolidation and rationalization of the resource extraction process has paralleled the increasing size and importance of nucleated settlements based on the timber industry. Settlement mobility has been an important feature in timber extraction, as floating logging camps have been used considerably over the past two decades. Settlement mobility is now beginning to decline due to an increasing emphasis on road transportation in the forest industry.

An important indicator of the changes in settlement morphology is the altered emphasis in movement from waterways to land and air routes. Improved market access, changing economi base, and centralization of settlement has markedly decreased the seasonality of many jobs in the study area. Social expressions of the trends identifiable during the period under consideration include population stabilization (increasing number of families as opposed to single male workers), expansion of community facilities, and incorporation of the three major settlements; Zeballos, in 1952, Gold River as an "instant" municipality in 1965, and Tahsis, in 197(

It is the cumulative settlement morphology of the Nootka Sound Region, expressing both the success and failure of human ambitions over the past seventy years, that is of primary interest in this paper.

The contemporary landscape of the region expresses the changes in resource demands, scale of settlement, and trans-portation that have occurred since the turn of the century, both in the immediate area and throughout coastal British Columbia. Trends identifiable within the study area reflect microcosmically events occuring elsewhere on the coast, although many regional disparities of both time and place obviously must be accounted for. The phases in settlement morphology identified in the paper could be applied to a larger-scale study encompassing the West Coast of Vancouver Island, or coastal British Columbia in its entirety. The

74

aper is designed specifically as a small-scale pilot project of such
coastal enquiry, utilizing the morphological approach.

METHODOLOGY

The study is based on evidence collected over a period
of three years. Documentary evidence includes government documents and other published and unpublished sources, including maps
and photographs from collections at the University of British
Columbia and the Provincial Archives. An example of documentation
rom a provincial government agency is the Nootka Land Registry,
acquired from the Director of Lands in Victoria. The Land Register
locuments all land alienations in the region since 1885.

Field research has involved on-site examination of all
settlement sites in order to ascertain their exact location, present
condition, and existing relationship with the regional pattern of
human occupance. Old logging float camp or shore camp locations
can be established by dating second-growth timber in logged areas
along the shoreline, and comparing results with entries in the
Nootka Land Register.

Interviews with pioneers in the region were also an
mportant aspect of field research, providing insights not readily
available in documentary sources.

The evidence for the picture of settlement presented
here is the result of a comparative analysis of documentary
sources, observations in the field, and interviews with pioneers
and with those currently working in the study area, verified by
reference to the Nootka Land Registry.

It should be pointed out that while the three develop-
mental stages in settlement morphology correspond roughly with
he designated time periods, the three stage sequence is primarily
an organizational convenience. The close of each period signifies
a lull in settlement development, when a previously extant settlement pattern was in a state of decline.

1900-1920: SPECULATION AND THE PIONEER FRINGE

The only permanent settlements in the Nootka Sound
Region at the turn of the century were four villages of Nootkan or
Aht indians, at Friendly Cove, (Yuquot) Nuchatlitz, Queen Cove,
and Ehedisaht, with an aggregate population of approximately
340. [2] Other sites were occupied during salmon runs, and at spring
herring spawnings, but many years of disease, warfare, and
missionization had resulted in abandonment of the yearly migratory
settlement pattern described by John Jewitt, one hundred years
previously. [3]

The Nootka Land Registry records speculative interest
in the Nootka Sound Region by Europeans as early as 1884, when
Edgar M. Sayward purchased 886 acres of timber at an aggregate
cost of $886.00. [4] Very little of this timber was exploited, but land
purchases increased in the area after 1909, when a marble quarry
was developed on Tlupana Arm. [5] Subsequently, an iron mine was
brought into production at Head Bay, on Tlupana Arm, owned
jointly by James Dunsmuir, then Lieutenant-Governor of British
Columbia, and Clarence Dawley, who also owned a trading post next
to the Indian reserve at Friendly Cove. [6]

Coal was known to exist close at hand to the south of
Nootka Sound, and limestone was plentiful throughout the area. The
real spur to speculative development, however, can be read in the
comments of Captain J. T. Walbran, writing in the Victoria
Colonist, November 14th, 1909:

> From Gold River to Campbell River a trail runs through
> a country in no place higher than 750 feet above sea level,
> and any railway passing from Victoria to the north of the
> island will, on account of the grade, necessarily pass
> within a few miles of Nootka Sound . . . . The country
> surrounding the Sound is covered by a dense growth of
> timber, suitable for export trade, and coal is found on
> the Estevan (Hesquiat) peninsula. Timber, limestone,
> marble, iron, and coal are known to exist in sufficient
> quantities to warrent the establishment of large
> industries. The port itself is so excellent, so easy of

76

approach from the ocean and so central that it is well up in the race for the terminous of a trans-continental railway.

That Captain Walbran's assertions were not just wishful thinking is verified in the Nootka Land Registry, which indicates 11,312 acres of land in the Gold River Valley were granted to the Esquimault and Nanaimo railway in 1913.[7]

Fifty land purchases were made between 1908 and 1913, mostly in the vicinity of Nootka Sound proper, the Gold River valley, and Muchalat Inlet. A total of sixty-nine pre-emptions were surveyed between 1912 and 1914, with the majority located on the seaward side of Nootka Island.[8]

The main reason for this land boom was the prospect of port and industrial facilities at a railhead on Nootka Sound. The institution of regular steamer service from Victoria via the C.P.R. S.S. Princess Macquinna, making West Coast points accessible to a land-hungry public, was also an important contributing factor.

European interest in settling Nootka Sound died in 1914, with the closing of both the marble quarry and the iron mine. Prospects for a railhead at Gold River proved to be disappointing, while settlers who pre-empted land on the seaward side of Nootka Island found farming an unrewarding venture. Some settlers of independent means stayed on, usually living along the sheltered inlets and bays. These were older people, seeking an independent, lonely life in the solitude of the west coast wilderness. Several examples of these settlers' homes, in various stages of decay, may be seen today along the shores of Esperanza Inlet.

The single most significant settlement development prior to the reduction plant boom of 1926 was the development of Nootka Cannery in 1917, three miles north of Friendly Cove, on Cook Channel. Developed by Everett Fishing Company of Everett, Washington State, the cannery was built on pilings, and boasted a hotel. During its heyday the Cannery employed about seventy-five people on shore, and an equivalent number as fishermen. These employees were principally single Chinese men on shore, and Indian fishermen and their families. On the foreshore behind the cannery, a squatter settlement developed, providing seasonal housing for Nootka Indians from more distant coastal villages.[9]

Nootka Cannery pioneered fish processing in the Nootka Sound Region by almost a decade, establishing fish as the primary resource. Lumbering and mining stagnated after the initial speculative interest died down, due to a lack of interest on the part of investors.

1920-1940: GOLD, AND THE RISE AND FALL OF THE PILCHARD

There was considerable interest in fish on the part of investors, however. In the six years following the end of the First World War, pilchards began appearing in considerable numbers all along the West Coast of Vancouver Island. Fishing companies wer quick to see the profits to be made from these fish, since they could be easily rendered into high-quality oil and fish meal. Nootk Cannery expanded its facilities to include a reduction plant, and its owners bolstered the sagging profits which had resulted from over-fishing salmon.

By 1927 five more settlements incorporating canneries and reduction plants had appeared in the Nootka Sound region, providing an aggregate seasonal population of approximately 1,000. The settlement focus, however, moved from the Nootka Cannery -- Friendly Cove area to Esperanza Inlet, where there were several sites suitable for cannery installation. (See Map 1.) The main criteria determining plant location were adequate supply of fresh water, flat land for building, and good dock sites.[10] Another implicit factor in plant location was the proximity of Indian fishermen, whose intimate "coastline knowledge" enabled them to make good money in the pilchard fishery.

The settlement at Experanza incorporated a hotel to serve visitors to the area, and therefore became the hub of social life in Esperanza Inlet. All the settlements were served by the S.S. Princess Macquinna, and by steamers owned by the various fish canning and packing companies.

78

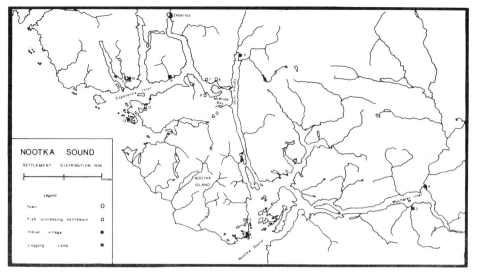

REFERENCES TO MAP # 1
(Nootka Sound, Settlement Distribution, 1936)

1. Friendly Cove Indian Village (Yuquot)
2. Nootka Cannery
3. Muchalat Logging Camp
4. Muchalat Indian Village
5. Tahsis Indian Village
6. Ceepeecee Cannery
7. Experanza Cannery & Hotel
8. Hecate Cannery
9. Ehedisaht Indian Village
10. Queen's Cove Indian Village
11. Queen's Cove Cannery
12. Nuchatlitz Cannery
13. Nuchatlitz Indian Village

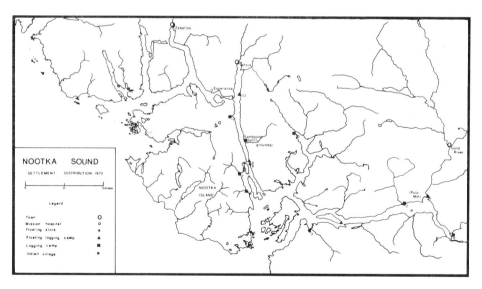

REFERENCES TO MAP # 2

0. Burman River - Logging Camp
1. Muchalat Indian Reserve
2. MuCurdy Creek - Logging Camp
3. Moya Bay - Logging Camp
4. Friendly Cove Indian Reserve
5. Malliard and Co. Floating Store
6. A Mangles Logging Float Camp
7. Kendrick Arm - Logging Camp
8. A. Rockwell Logging Float Camp
9. O'Hara - Logging Float Camp
10. Head Bay - Logging Camp
11. Blowhole Bay - Logging Camp
12. G. Green - Logging Float Camp
13. Nuchatlitz Indian Reserve
14. Malliard and Co. Floating Store
15. Queen's Cove Indian Reserve

The pilchard boom began to taper off in the early 1930's.[11] Salmon runs declined also, and the dry salteries set up in temporary quarters around the shores of Esperanza Inlet shared the fate of the salmon canneries and reduction plants, which closed down one by one during the 1930's and early war years.[12] Nootka Cannery managed to stay in operation until 1951, when it too ceased functioning and its machinery was dismantled.

The declining pilchard runs and increasingly unprofitable salmon fisheries spurred prospecting in the Nootka Sound region during the early 1930's. Many unemployed fishermen and cannery workers took to prospecting and trapping to bolster their sagging incomes. Gold had been discovered in the Zeballos Valley in 1924, and by 1932 several properties had been developed.[13] High assay returns prompted a gold rush in 1936, and the village of Zeballos grew in two years from a collection of shacks to a population of well over one thousand. While profits from fishing and fish processing declined, mining accelerated in importance. Esperanza Hotel, founded to serve the interests of cannery workers, took on new importance as a staging point for the Zeballos Valley gold claims. The cannery at Ceepeecee (Canadian Packing Corporation) also acquired new importance as a result of the Zeballos boom: gold concentrates and gold bricks were shipped on the S.S. Princess Macquinna from the Ceepeecee dock until a government wharf was installed in Zeballos in 1938.

Although a total of twenty-eight properties were developed, the principle mines were Privateen, Spud Valley, Reno and Mount Zeballos. By the time gold mining shut down in 1948 when the government pegged the price of gold at thirty-five dollars per ounce, gold bricks worth eleven million dollars and gold concentrates worth two million dollars had been shipped to Victoria on the Princess Macquinna.[14]

The year 1938 marks the rather tentative beginnings of sawmilling in Nootka Sound on a large-scale, permanent basis. Prior to this time, lumbering had been carried out on a small-scale, mobile basis. A small mill was set up to serve Zeballos, but no one had considered an export mill involving considerable capital investment feasible.

80

Port Tahsis at McBride Bay on Nootka Island was developed by a group of British investors incorporated under the name Nootka Wood Products. This company acquired a considerable number of Timber Licences in the Nootka Sound region, and arranged for local loggers to supply the mill. The venture only lasted one year. Lack of space, inadequate facilities for waste elimination, and untreated hemlock pilings which had a tendency to rot in a few months forced closure. Insolvency was apparently a contributing factor also. The mill did prove one thing in its short career which had an important effect on developing settlement patterns: deep-sea ships were willing to call at Nootka Sound to pick up timber for export, making sawmilling in the region a worthwhile enterprise. Isolation from domestic markets and processing facilities precluded extensive timber development prior to the close of the 1930's. Also, mechanized logging techniques were insufficiently developed to handle the steep terrain before this time. Investors were not willing to commit capital to such an isolated area when more lucrative regions nearer to domestic markets and established processing facilities were closer at hand. The Second World War created an alternate source of investment, in the form of the Federal Government, which provided an unprecedented impetus to development.

1940-1970: ESTABLISHMENT OF THE TIMBER HEGEMONY

The fourth decade of the twentieth century marks the beginning of a new theme in the development of Nootka Sound settlement. The Second World War made timber, especially airplane spruce, a high priority item for the Canadian Government. Gordon Gibson's timber company purchased the machinery from the bankrupt Port Tahsis Mill, and more important, they acquired rights to the Timber Licences previously held by Nootka Wood Products. The mill machinery was moved to Tahsis, at the head of Tahsis Inlet, the valley behind which supplied ample timber. Logging was done on a "cost-plus" basis during the war years, with most capital expenditures charged to the "Spruce Account."[15]

The Nootka Sound region developed rapidly during the war years, since gold, timber, and fish were all in demand for the war effort. However, the canneries and reduction plants, with the one exception, mentioned earlier, were all shut down by

81

the end of the war for two main reasons. One was the development of fast, efficient packing ships with refrigerated brine tanks which could carry fish directly to large processing plants in developed urban areas; and the second reason was the drastic decline of the pilchard fisheries, and badly depleted salmon stocks.

By 1948, the landscape in the Nootka Sound region was already dotted with derelict settlements. Besides the abandonment of fish processing plants, the Indian village of Ehedisaht was abandoned after the war, and the inhabitants moved into the buildings deserted after mining in Zeballos ended.

1948 also marks the year in which Tahsis Company was formed, through a "fifty-fifty" partnership between Gordon Gibson and his shipping agents, East Asiatic Steamship Lines. The partnership developed after the Tahsis Sawmill burned down in 1947, and Gibson needed a partner in order to rebuild. Gibson terminated the Tahsis Company partnership in 1952, in a dispute over the company acquisition of Tree Farm Licence 19, whereupon East Asiatic bought out his fifty-percent share.

The population of Zeballos was about two hundred in 1952, and was supported primarily by Manning Timber Company, which acquired Timber Licences in the Zeballos River valley after mining closed down, and by the village's liquor store, the only one in the whole region. Tahsis was a company town of about eight hundred people, with a new export mill and a deep sea wharf. The fish processing industry was no more. Logging camps subcontracting to Tahsis Company were developing the increased timber quota offered by T.F.L. 19. Experanza's semi-defunct hotel burned down, and was replaced by a regional hospital operated by the Shantymen's Christian Association of Victoria. Fishermen still used Tahsis and Zeballos as headquarters, but sold their catches to cash buyers who stayed only for the season. During the early 1950's floating stores replaced the cannery settlements, which previously incorporated both buying a supply functions. 1952 saw the end of the S.S. Princess Macquinna, which finally, after forty years service, could not muster steam for another trip. She was replaced by the Northland Prince, a much smaller vessel operating from Vancouver

Tahsis Company became the main employer and hence the major economic influence on settlement patterns during the decade 1950-1960. Camps were established in sheltered bays and at river mouths, from which road networks were pushed into the logging areas. "A"-framing also continued to be used to log licences directly accessible from the water.

Settlement patterns underwent no real morphological changes between 1952 and 1965. Tahsis mill production increased, and more families moved into the town. Tahsis Company concentrated on developing holdings in the Gold River area, re-locating their old logging camp of Muchalat from Jacklah Creek to the mouth of the Gold River. By 1965 the population of Muchalat had risen to four hundred, including several families. A private road to the East Coast of Vancouver Island had been completed before 1965, providing easy access to Campbell River.

Expanded markets, coupled with more highly mechanized logging techniques, sent Tahsis Company in search of a partner to build a pulp mill at the mouth of Gold River. In 1965 work was started in clearing the millsite. Canadian International Paper Ltd., a subsidiary of International Paper of New York, was chosen as a partner, acquiring a half-interest in the expanded Tahsis Company. In 1967 T.F.L. 19 was enlarged to accommodate the pulp mill, over the bitter protests of other Vancouver Island loggers.[16] The Gold River townsite, at the junction of the Gold and Heber Rivers, was planned and constructed over a three year period (1966-1968) and presently has a population of approximately twenty-four hundred people. The town of Gold River was an "instant municipality," achieving this status immediately to avoid being stigmatized as a company town. Tahsis followed suit, finally, in 1970.

SUMMARY

The settlement morphology of the Nootka Sound Region has been characterized by a high rate of settlement mortality during the first five decades of the period under consideration. The last two decades have emphasized the themes of consolidation and regional integration of resource extraction industries, and human communities expanded or developed during this period have exhibited similar tendencies towards centralization and consolidation.

The first period of non-indian settlement development

occurring roughly between the years 1900-1920 emphasized small scale, dispersed settlement, principally speculative and short-term in nature. Homesteads, timber leases, and mineral workings declined drastically when improved access to Nootka Sound was not forthcoming.

The second period was pioneered by Nootka Cannery in 1917, and was characterized by settlements clustered around canneries and pilchard reduction plants. The closing decade of the second period (1930-1940) was characterized by decline in fish processing plants, and by the Zeballos gold rush. Export saw-milling was attempted, but failed.

The period 1940-1970 was initially marked by a rapid upswing in the lumber industry, and the elimination of mining and fish processing as viable bases for settlement. The last two decades are typified by further expansion and consolidation by the lumber industry, direct removal of fish to canneries in urban areas and stagnation of the mining industry (except for the period 1962 - 1969, when Zeballos produced pelletized iron ore for Japan).

Technological change over the last three decades has emphasized road and air transportation, although water transport has remained very important.

The overall themes emphasized in the settlement morphology of the Nootka Sound Region are: modification of settlement patterns according to changes in resource demand and availability; growth in the size of settlements; and changes in social organization of settlements, including an increasing number of families and the incorporation of three municipalities. The land scape of the study area expresses these changes in a pattern of deserted and occupied settlements, reflecting in microcosm similar changes in evidence throughout coastal British Columbia.

The format and conclusions of this paper serve as a pilot project for a study encompassing a much larger area, using data from sources similar to those utilized here. Such a study would provide the first comprehensive survey of the coastal settlement morphology of British Columbia.

REFERENCES

1. These boundaries are the same as the Nootka Land District.

2. Moser, Charles, Vancouver Island's West Coast, (Victoria, 1926), p. 142.

3. Brown, R., A Narrative of the Adventures and Sufferings of John R. Jewitt, (London, 1896).

   (For an examination of Nootkan population declines see White, B. P. "The Decline of the Moachat: A Geographical Analysis of the Changing Nootkan World View, from Pre-Contact Times to Missionization." Unpublished M.S., 1971.)

4. Nootka Land Register, Director of Lands, Victoria, p. 18.

5. Walbran, J. T., "Historic Nootka," The Daily Colonist, November 14th, 1909.

6. Nootka Land Register, Director of Lands, Victoria, p. 62.

7. Ibid., pp. 44-46.   8. Ibid., pp. 59-84.

9. Sharcott, Margaret, "Nootka's Silver Harvest," The Daily Colonist, May 31st, 1970, pp. 6-7.

   (See also B. C. Archives Photo Collection.)

10. Ibid., p. 6.

11. Nicholson, George, Vancouver Island's West Coast, 1762-1962, (Victoria: Morriss Printing Co., 1968), p. 244.

12. Ibid., pp. 245-246.

13. Stevenson, J. S., Vancouver Island, Zeballos River Section, Minister of Mines, Victoria, Annual Report, 1935.

14. Nicholson, op. cit., p. 302.

15. "Cost plus" meant a guaranteed profit margin for operators under contract to the government. The "Spruce Accoun allowed capital equipment expenses to be charged to the government, enabling operators to mechanize rapidly.

16. See McMurray, R., "Tahsis Log Bid Bares Rivalries," The Vancouver Province, August 27th, 1965.

ON THE CENTRIFUGAL ORIENTATION OF THE DISTRIBUTION OF GOODS AND SERVICES

L. J. Evenden
Simon Fraser University

INTRODUCTION

The wave of enthusiasm which has characterized research along Central Place theoretical lines in urban geography appeared to crest in the early years of the last decade. It was then that studies from various parts of the world, carried out with an increasing tendency to standardized methodologies, were being reported in larger numbers. They demonstrated that Central Place Theory could be of great benefit in understanding certain urban location factors and tertiary distribution patterns but, simultaneously, they cautioned that new circumstances were being found which made simplistic applications of the theory unsatisfactory.[1] In the same period a convergence of interests became evident with anthropological and other research on marketing in parts of the "under-developed" world.[2] At present it seems that a new period of consolidation of empirical findings lies ahead of us, before any expanded applicability of Central Place Theory becomes known.

Among the more important empirical findings which complicate any application of the theory are cultural and social variations among groups of people,[3] the mobility and periodicity of centres of distribution,[4] and the landscape infrastructure itself.[5] Each of these has been shown to have a significant bearing upon the ranges and distributions of goods and services in the areas where they were studied. For example, an explicit argument concerning the relation between the range of a good and the mobility of the point of distribution itself is made by Stine.[6] Stine argues that if mobility is conceived as varying from high to low (rather than merely contrasted between mobile or not mobile) then the maximum range and minimum range i.e. threshold, may be taken to determine when a function becomes mobile or fixed in its establishment form. Thus if the maximum range is greater than the minimum, the establishment is fixed because profits accrue from sales beyond the minimum range or threshold. But if the maximum range is less than the minimum, the establishment may either cease operations or may become mobile, "jumping" from one place to another for short periods at each place and, in this way, "piecing together" a profitable existence or at least surviving. Thus the question of mobility leads directly into problems of periodicity.

But empirical variations appear to be numerous. Even without regard to the complications of traditional periodic and itinerant forms of distribution which follow complicated calendars in many parts of the world, two modern studies may be cited from northern Europe to illustrate the empirical variability. Helle has reported that in northern Finland a good proportion of the distribution of retail goods is effected by mobile shops but that this distribution form is most fully developed in ". . . densely settled rural areas . . . ." He notes further that ". . . mobile shops are used more generally only after a trip to a fixed shop is over five times as long as a trip to the selling point of a mobile shop. '[7] Wheeler, in a study set in Sutherland County, Scotland, concludes almost the opposite: that it is because of the light population densities in the area that mobile shops are necessary. Further, their existence and persistence in Sutherland relate to traditions of itinerant marketing both by road and by coastal boats, and thus the relevance of transport types, costs, and levels of personal mobility is implied. [8]

A SCOTTISH CASE STUDY

The present writer proposes to study patterns of distribution by mobile shops in South-East Scotland. This is an area characterized by a considerable variety of non-urban population densities (from uninhabited to 98.0 persons per square mile in 1961), by a network of small towns to which people travel for shopping and other services, and by a very marked degree of mobi shop retailing emanating from these towns.

Mobile shops are more than mere delivery vans; they are small but fully equipped shops-on-wheels which may be quite specialized as to whether they sell meat, bake goods, groceries, hardware, and so on. In general, shops follow prescribed routes, calling at regular customers. In the case of mobile shops belonging to co-operative societies, they call at member's houses. Advance orders are not necessary and of course incidental hawking of goods is not precluded.

Almost all of the mobile shops in the region are sponsored by fixed shops in the towns, the latter depending to varying degrees for their own economic viability upon the operation of their "vans." For example, there appears to be a tendency for fixed shops in declining central places (with 1961 populations under 2,000) to encourage their vans to seek wider custom in the country-side. The inference may be made that the maximum range is contracting and, as it approaches the minimum range, the mobile arm of the enterprise is activated "in advance" in order to forestall uneconomic operation. Thus in this area and example, as well as in those reported by Helle and Wheeler, Stine's suggested explanation would need considerable elaboration; for both forms of distribution, fixed and mobile, may co-exist within the same establishment and, by implication, the range of a good may vary for the same good within the same establishment, the only difference being the direction and manner of distribution. Where a good is purchased at a centre by a customer, the usually-assumed centripetal character of movement prevails; but where a good is taken from the centre to a customer at a location away from the central place, the present context of centrifugal distribution is recognized.

Preliminary enquiry has suggested two general approaches in which further understanding of centrifugal distribution may be pursued. [9]

The first relates to the infrastructure of landscape, implying road access and residential building concentrations. It is suggested that a centrifugally-oriented distribution system will "select" locations by size and accord the larger places "preferential" treatment through more frequent calls. This suggestion

reflects the traditional countryside residential pattern in southern
Scotland. Typically, one to about fifteen households may be
located together, in adjoining cottages, on one site, in the shadow
of the "big house" where the farm owner of manager may reside.
Where the number of households is large, the membership in co-
operative societies (which sponsor many of the mobile shops)
probably will be more numerous at any location; also there will be
more households which do not belong to the co-operative but which
may provide an increased possibility of incidental hawking of goods
In both cases, time and distance costs between sales are minimize
It follows that the total relevant demand to be met from a central
place in such a landscape is that which may be served at points
along routes rather than the commonly assumed aggregate of dema
within areas. These points are illustrated in Figures 1 and 2.
Figure 1 shows the greater emphasis placed upon a centre with a
larger population as compared with that placed upon a lesser centr
Figure 2 illustrates the suggestion that easy road access is more
responsible than population distribution for greater frequencies of
contacts with central places.

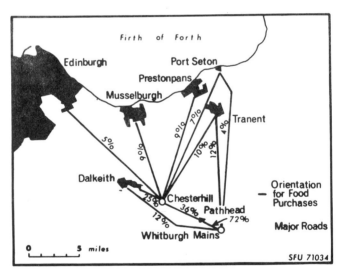

Fig. 1   To show the more widespread central
place contacts of settlements with larger
populations. (Population of Chesterhill 112;
Whitburgh Mains 25)

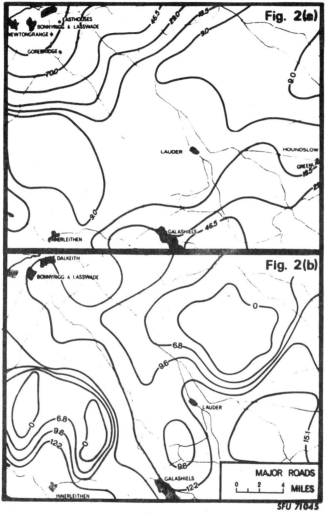

Figure 2. The relationship between road access and
frequency of contact with central places for
food purchases in part of south-east Scotland.

Isopleth values represent persons per square mile (2a.) and frequency
of weekly food purchase contacts (2b.).

The implied suggestion that status differences within the population may be reflected in housing styles and magnitudes is one which has merit in the study area. The population may be differentiated along lines of social status into two broad groups, farm labourers and other workers, and farm owners or managers. Between these two groups the pattern of automobile ownership varies and the levels of personal mobility consequently vary. Further, the first named group tends to belong to co-operative societies more typically and relies upon mobile shops more fully. Both groups are served by mobile shops, however, and often more than one shop selling the same provisions will call at the same location, the one selling to the "big house" and the other to the "cottages." At the extreme, this may double the cost of distribution to that point. Because these shops characteristically serve households falling within only one of the two status groups noted, it is suggested that this distributional overlap is determined less by economic forces than by motives rooted in social status. The fact that the system may remain economically viable permits its continuation in practice and suggests the existence of "excess profits." In the permissive space-economic circumstances of "excess profits" and in the less permissive but locally well-understood area of social convention, "optimum solutions" for routing will be less a matter of network geometry than of nuances of social interaction. "Optimum solutions" therefore may be expected to vary and carry implications for the explanation of the ranges of goods.

The two approaches which frame this study may now be summarized.

1. Landscape infrastructure asserts itself in the patterns of goods and services distribution with larger points of settlement being emphasized through more frequent provisioning by mobile shops.

2. Routing patterns of varying optima will characterize the structure of goods and services distribution by mobile shops, the variations being expressions of social status differences in the population.

It is suggested that enquiry within these approaches may further our understanding of the patterned inter-dependencies which exist among men, their institutions and their landscapes.

REFERENCES

1. The trends noted are also reflected in Berry's bood, Geography of Market Centers and Retail Distribution (Prentice-Hall, 1967), by the organization of Chapters 3-6.

2. A particularly important study in this regard is that by G. W. Skinner, "Marketing and Social Structure in Rural China," Journal of Asian Studies, XXIV, (1964-65), #1, pp. 3-43; #2, pp. 195-228; #3, pp. 363-399.

3. A study which investigates these differences within a Canadian setting is R. A. Murdie's "Cultural Differences in Consumer Travel," Economic Geography, XLI, (1965), pp. 211-233.

4. See especially Stine, J. H. "Temporal Aspects of Tertiary Distribution Elements in Korea," in Forrest R. Pitts (ed.), Urban Systems and Economic Development, Eugene, University of Oregon, School of Business Administration, (1962), pp. 68-88.

5. Johnston, R. J. 'Central Places and the Settlement Pattern," Annals, A.A.G., LVI, (1966), pp. 541-549.

6. The range of a good may be expressed as the maximum distance out from a central place that a good may be marketed before increasing transfer costs from the centre, and/or competition from an alternate centre, prevent its further sale.

7. Helle, R., 'Retailing in Rural Northern Finland: Particularly by Mobile Shops," Fennia, XCI, No. 3, (1964), 120 pp. plus map.

8. Wheeler, P. T. "Travelling Vans and Mobile Shops in Sutherland," Scottish Geographical Magazine, LXXXVI, (1960), pp. 147-155.

9. Evenden, L. J. The Settlement Hierarchy in South-east Scotland, unpublished Ph.D. Thesis, University of Edinburgh, (1970), 436 pp.

THE TRANSITION FROM HOME OWNERSHIP TO RENTAL STATUS: THE FACTOR OF HOUSE SIZE

Robert Christensen
University of Washington

INTRODUCTION

In cities, residential land occupies more space than any other land use type. Yet, residential land itself is of many kinds ranging from high to low value areas. Within these areas, there are dwellings of varying shape and size. Moreover, there are owner and renter-occupied dwellings. This paper will examine the changing ownership status of "single-family dwellings" as this relates to house size. The study area is the Seattle Wallingford district located about one mile west of the University of Washington and four miles north of the Seattle central business district.

STUDY AREA

The study area (Figure 1) has a substantial percentage of rental and owner/rental dwellings. It also contains an appreciable house size variation; thus it appears to provide a good laboratory for the purposes at hand.

Within the Seattle area, only four percent of housing in high value areas is in rental status. By contrast, in poverty housing areas over forty percent is rental. In middle value areas about fourteen percent of the housing is rental.[1] Figure 2 indicates this general relationship as it pertains to the percent of single-family rental dwellings within different value housing areas. In 1951, the Wallingford study area had nineteen percent rental housing. In 1969, thirty-five percent of the housing was rental.

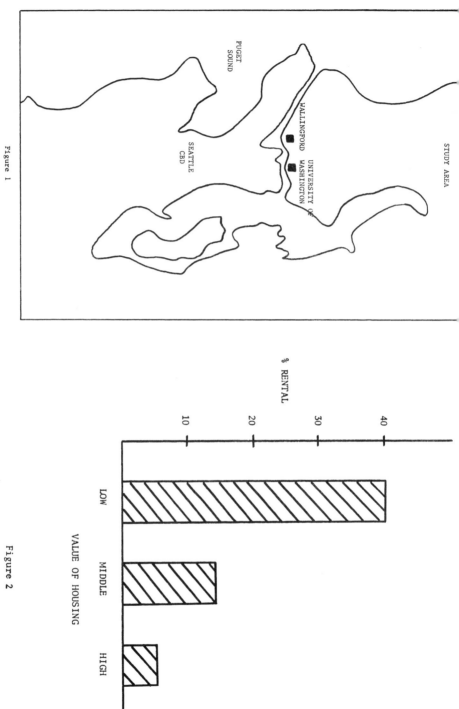

Figure 1

Figure 2

The average dwelling size also varies with different
value residential housing areas. As might be expected, high value
housing areas have a greater average dwelling size than the lower
value areas. But what of the variance or deviation from the
average size within a particular residential area itself? Figure 3
depicts some comparative size deviations. These deviations were
computed using the average number of rooms per owner-occupied
dwelling per census block with each typical residential area.[2] The

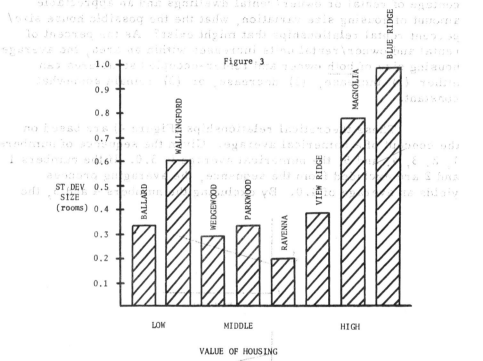

Figure 3

single-family owner-occupied dwellings within the Ballard residential area show little variation in size. Wallingford, the study area,
indicates a more significant variation then the other low value
housing areas. Wedgewood, Parkwood, and Ravenna (all middle
value areas) also show little size deviation from their average.
The high value areas of Magnolia and Blue Ridge show a large
amount of housing size deviation. Figure 3 shows that a greater
degree of size deviation occurs in high value housing areas. The
Wallingford area is the only exception to this latter statement.
However, if we examine this area, we find that it was, in fact, a

high value neighborhood in its initial development. Thus, our study area is perhaps indicative of the breakup to rental status of a former high value housing area, as this particularly relates to housing size.

METHODOLOGY

Given a residential area containing a substantial percentage of rental or owner/rental dwellings and an appreciable amount of housing size variation, what the the possible house size/ percent rental relationships that might exist? As the percent of rental and owner/rental units increases within an area, the average housing size of both owner and renter-occupied structures can either (1) increase, (2) decrease, or (3) remain somewhat constant.

These theoretical relationships (Figure 4) are based on the concept of a numerical average. Given the sequence of numbers 1, 2, 3, 4, and 5, the numerical average is 3.0. If the numbers 1 and 2 are excluded from the sequence, the averaging process yields an average of 4.0. By excluding the numbers 4 and 5, the

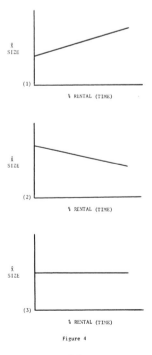

Figure 4

average becomes 2.0. Thus, the exlusion of the smallest and largest numbers within a numerical sequence, yields a respective increase and decrease in the average of the remaining numbers.

As pertaining to the house size/percent rental relationships, an increase in the average housing size implies that the smaller dwellings are becoming rentals first. If the average size decreases, the opposite is true. If the average house size remains somewhat the same, the implication is that equal numbers of large and small homes are becoming rental units concurrently.

To examine the house size/percent rental relationship within the Wallingford area, it is necessary to collect data showing the size and occupancy status over time for all single-family dwellings.

A LOOK AT WALLINGFORD

Let us look at the Wallingford study area and examine the house size/percent rental relationship. The housing size data was obtained from the King County Residential Tax Assessor Department, Seattle, Washington. This size was recorded as square footage (porch, garage, and basement excluded) for each dwelling unit. The differentiation between owner and renter-occupied structures was accomplished for three time periods (1951, 1960, 1969) using the Polk's Seattle City Directory.[3] As indicated in Figure 5, as the percent of rental and owner/rental units increased within the study area, the average size of both the owner and renter units decreased. In 1951, there was nineteen percent rental and owner/rental housing within the Wallingford area. The average owner-occupied house size was 1186 square feet; the average renter-occupied size was 1667 square feet. There was twenty-four percent rental housing within the study area in 1960 and the average renter-occupied house size had decreased to 1552 square feet. Between 1951 and 1960, the average owner size remained constant. By 1969, the percent of rental housing had increased to thirty-five percent. At this time, the average housing sizes of the owner and renter-occupied dwellings were less than the averages of both 1951 and 1960. Thus, the larger structures have become rentals first. This is consistent with the second relationship depicted in Figure 4.

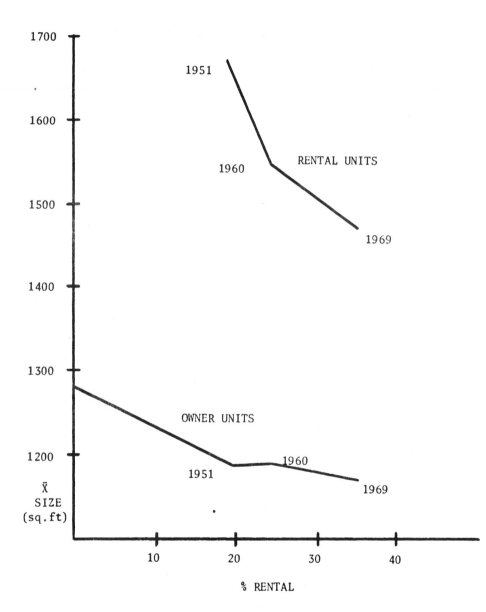

Figure 5

Why have the largest single-family dwellings within the Wallingford study area become rentals first? One might too quickly answer that large dwellings afford greater possibilities for being cut-up into apartment-type units. Perhaps, one should first ask, why do houses in general, become rental units?

General population aging is a dynamic feature of residential structure use. Young adults commonly experience increasing family size and thus require expanding housing accommodations. With older adults, the opposite is true. Having raised their children, and nearing retirement, many are faced with the decision of what to do with their existing home. They can elect to (1) remain in the dwelling, (2) supplement the occupancy of their home (rent rooms or cut-up the dwelling into "apartments"), or (3) move from their home, in which case, the house may continue in owner status or become rental property. As Boyce states in a study examining residential change in Seattle, "most often a house becomes a rental as a result of its nonsaleability, perhaps due to deterioration, overpricing, or the general neighborhood. Sometimes houses are kept as a source of income or for speculation purposes, perhaps awaiting a change in zoning as to commercial property, or the demand for land for other uses."[4]

In 1969, the average number of families per rental or owner/rental structure within the Wallingford study area was 1.6. Thus, most of the rental dwellings provided living accommodations for more than one family. Interviews with local real estate agencies provide explanation for this family average. The owner/renter structures are usually such that the owner does not want to move or need to move, even though the dwelling is too large for his needs. Rental possibilities occur because of the proximity of the University of Washington, and thus, the owner remains using the house as a source of income by supplementing the occupancy of the home. There are also strictly rental dwellings within the area purchased by an investor and occupied by groups of students, some of which are clearly communal living participants. Both the owner/renter and strictly renter-occupied structures involve students. With the University of Washington so near, one would expect this rental demand and house size/percent rental relationship to appear. Thus, within the Wallingford area, there are two primary reasons for the larger homes becoming rental units first: home owners supplementing the occupancy of their homes, and the investor.

CONCLUSIONS

Having examined the house size/percent rental relation-ship within one residential area of Seattle, it would seem appropriate for the curious urban geographer to examine other areas. What are the factors influencing the transition from home ownership to rental status in these areas? Do the largest dwellings become rentals first, or is it the smaller dwellings?

REFERENCES

1. Ronald R. Boyce, Residency Change in Seattle, 1962-1967, Research Report No. 3, Social Change Evaluation Project (Seattle: University of Washington Press, 1968), p. 70.

2. Block Statistics Census Data, City of Seattle, June 1963, Urban Data Center Project (Seattle: University of Washington, 1963).

3. Polk's Seattle City Directory (Los Angeles: R. L. Polk & Co., Publishers, 1951, 1960, 1969).

4. Boyce, op. cit., p. 72.

CENTRALIZATION AND SOVIET REGIONAL DEVELOPMENT

Robert N. North
University of British Columbia

INTRODUCTION

This paper summarizes the aims, methodology and some conclusions of a larger piece of work. It then focuses more closely on one aspect of that work -- centralization -- which is still at an early stage of development in the writer's thinking. The paper is therefore presented primarily as a discussion paper.

How are differences between political-economic systems reflected spatially? In particular, how are they reflected in comparative patterns of regional economic development -- the kind of change which is measured by coefficients of redistribution or shift ratios? With respect to the Soviet Union the question takes the form: are there features of soviet regional development which we would not have expected to find if the past 50 years had seen a continuation of tsarist rule, or perhaps an evolved parliamentary democracy, something like the present Canadian system? The question seems to be particularly relevant in the soviet case, for two reasons. Firstly, the Soviet Union has always claimed to have definite goals for the spatial development of the economy, unlike many other countries.[1] Secondly, for soviet theoreticians it is an article of faith that a socialist system will achieve a better balance between regions than a capitalist system. (The term 'better' may be taken to include among other things a more even spatial distribution of capital investment and more rounded development of each region.[2])

The term 'political-economic system' requires definition. Adapting the ideas of Grossman and Buckingham, we

103

take it to comprise three elements: institutions (that is to say, rules of conduct, established ways of thinking, and organisational structures), an ideology (a set of ideas on social reality; values and goals to strive for or maintain), and a strategy or set of preferred methods for pursuing the goals.[3] Grossman's definition would perhaps be narrower, covering only the institutions. However that is just a question of semantics as far as this paper is concerned. Any attempt to find out what constitutes the 'sovietness' of soviet regional development must of necessity examine all three -- institutions, ideology and strategy -- and all three are thoroughly interlocked.

LONG-TERM TRENDS, GOALS AND STRATEGIES

There is no single obvious way of tackling the kind of question asked in this paper. The writer first examined long-term regional development trends in the Soviet Union, combining several admittedly problem-ridden approaches and focussing on soviet ideology and strategies as potential explanatory variables rather than on institutions. The investigation went through the following stages:-

1. A description of comparative regional development is the Soviet Union since 1917, in terms of the shift of activities between regions and the changing composition of activities in each region -- using the official Major Economic Regions or similar units.

2. An examination of this picture in relation to stated soviet goals for spatial economic development -- and national goals with spatial implications -- and in relation to the develop ment strategies chosen. The objective was to see whether strategies and actual developments followed logically from stated goals.

3. An attempt to project the pre-revolutionary economic geography of Russia (or in fact, of selected regions within it) to the present day under different kinds of government. This was done using a export-base approach.[4]

4. A comparison of the development of soviet regions with

that of selected regions elsewhere in the world. The regions were selected for their similarity before 1917.[5]

The third and fourth stages obviously involve highly speculative argument. Elbert Bowden examined techniques of long-term projection two years ago in the <u>Annals of Regional Science</u> and pinpointed the main problem: unpredictable change in so many variables that almost any outcome is possible.[6] The historical-geographical analogue approach, in Chorley's terms, is extremely noisy -- there are too many variables.[7] These approaches are useful for stimulating ideas as to what might be worth examining more closely by other means, but that is probably as far as they can be taken. In this case it was interesting that while the soviet and supposedly analogous regions in fact developed differently (outlying regions tended to receive more attention and more industry in the Soviet Union) it generally proved easy to project the pre-revolutionary situation to something resembling that of the present day, even assuming a tsarist or Canadian type of government. Assumptions of similar technology and similar desires to develop industry and maintain national strength proved sufficient.

The major problem faced in the first two stages was to define the system inductively -- in other words to identify a coherent set of goals and strategies, or even just goals, which could be called the soviet package. Soviet spatial goals and goals with spatial implications emerged as a complex of opposing forces, of fluctuating and variously interpreted priorities. It proved possible to identify forces working for and against the spatial concentration of economic activities, for example -- such as the objective of rapid national industrial growth on the one hand, and goals for the economic growth of outlying regions on the other hand. Furthermore the accepted interpretations of certain broadly-stated goals for regional development have changed considerably with changing technology and the growth of planning experience. There appeared to be very few goals which have been unwaveringly held, and consistently interpreted and implemented, during soviet times. As one might expect in consequence, there are also few spatial trends which have been consistently maintained during soviet times.

If this is so, is the whole search for "peculiarly soviet" features of regional development shown to be useless? Not

105

necessarily. What does seem to be pointless is any attempt to seek long-term consistency or regular progression through time. Even more pointless is analysis in terms of inevitabilities, historical imperatives or the inexorable march of progress, which soviet and even some western writers still sometimes attempt. Determinism may be considered a dead issue in geography; elsewhere it apparently is not. In an article in World Politics last year, Alexander Eckstein stated that "the stage of economic development imposes certain imperatives of its own on any economic, political and social system, including Communist ones."[8]

INSTITUTIONAL INFLUENCES

The search for long-term consistent goals and spatial trends may not be very fruitful. However, any specific scheme or series of schemes for regional development, such as the Ural-Kuznetsk Combine or the Virgin Lands Scheme, can be analysed in terms of the forces tending to push key investment decisions in certain directions. Spatial goals then become one of several group of such forces, together with technological constraints, social and demographic trends, and so forth. This brings us to the fifth stage of our attempt to identify spatial peculiarities of the soviet system, and introduces the role of institutions. It is the institutional arrangements which determine how these various groups of forces impinge on the key decision-makers -- and indeed, help to decide who will be the decision makers. One would not wish to suggest that the nature of regional development can be deduced from the nature of institutions. Their influence cannot be so specific. Nevertheless they form an important and too-little-studied group of forces in regional development. Isard and his associates have examined them on the theoretical level in the recently published General Theory;[9] they are also worth more empirical study.

In the soviet case four kinds of institutions seem particularly important in regional development. The first is the distribution of decision making on capital investment; the second, particularly since one feature of that distribution is extreme centralization, is the arrangements for obtaining information for decision-makers; the third is the distribution of fund-raising powers between levels of government; and the fourth is the arrangements for debate on controversial issues before decisions are made

The rest of this paper briefly examines the first of these, concentrating on the effects of centralization of decision-making power with respect to capital investments. The degree of centralization has varied considerably during soviet times, both spatially and sectorally, but we have time here only to touch on a few general aspects.

CENTRALIZATION

We can make four generalizations about the effects of centralization. Firstly, the more power is concentrated in the hands of the central government, the less is the potential for independent action by such groups as entrepreneurs, regional authorities and consumers. This may reduce the sensitivity of the economy to demands at the regional level, which has certainly happened in the Soviet Union. It has proved difficult to balance the regional supply of, and demand for, items ranging from clothing to building stone, and co-ordination at the regional level of industries with potential for linkage has been very poor.

Secondly, changing the concentration of power changes the set of considerations faced by decision makers. In some ways the range broadens with centralization. For example, authorities deciding where to locate industry may also be responsible for transport and housing, though they may not have to worry about competition from other industrialists. This point can be illustrated by an example from transport. In some remote parts of the Soviet Union regional transport seems to be based more heavily on helicopters than one might expect from the amount and importance of traffic. Perhaps this is because the government sets off against the high cost, the reduced need to maintain roads and keep them open in winter. A potential private-enterprise helicopter operator in another country would see only part of a similar regional transport situation, but he would have to assess potential competition. On the other hand he, not knowing conditions elsewhere or preferring to live in the particular region, might run a service in circumstances where a national authority might switch resources elsewhere to meet set traffic or profit targets.)

If responsibilities spread too widely there may be internal conflicts of interest. For example, labour turnover in the

107

new Siberian oilfields has been very high, partly because of poor housing. One reason for the poor housing is that housing funds were channelled through the oil and geological ministries, whose performance was measured by rate of oil production and discovery -- but not by rate of housing construction.

Generalising from these two examples, we can expect differences between more and less centralised systems both in the ordering of priorities, and in methods of calculating the costs and benefits of alternative measures. Theoretically the more centralis system should be less likely to produce wasteful duplication of the kind exemplified by the wells on North American oilfields; in practice this advantage seems to be balanced by poorer flexibility, slower response to local changes and the tendency for important considerations to become submerged.

Thirdly, the greater the concentration of power, the greater the potential influence of an individual decision-maker's capriciousness, miscalculations or brilliance. It might be argued that bad capricious decisions generally bring only short-term chan̨ as in the more foolhardy parts of the Virgin Lands Scheme, but there may be an inertial effect of installed capital.

Fourthly, the greater the concentration of power, the greater the scope for concerted effort towards any goal. On the on hand this may help eliminate wasteful duplication and diffusion of effort: this may be true of some soviet transport developments. On the other hand, if leaders are ill-advised or capricious, it may lead to massive, ill-considered capital investment as, apparently, in the case of many of Khrushchev's chemical works. Whether the Ural-Kuznetsk Combine comes into this category is a moot point, since another aspect of the scope for concerted effort is that such projects, if initially unsuccessful, can be subsidized until additiona developments create a justification for them. In other words capit risk and relative rates of return are less crucial considerations than in a less centralized economy, and it is easier to take a very long-term view. Obviously this is even more the case when centralization is so extreme that there is no periodic accounting to an electorate with choice.

The third and fourth points just made suggest that we

may expect highly-centralized economies to be particularly
unpredictable over the long term, during which leaders change.
Certainly in the Soviet Union we tend to associate particular trends
in development, including regional development, with particular
leaders. Apart from this, perhaps the most important differences
between more and less centralized systems is likely to be in the
relative timing of developments, stemming from a different
ordering of priorities even when, so to speak, the total shopping
list is similar. If the relative timing of developments is different,
then the surrounding conditions will be different when each development takes place. This may strongly affect the form and effects
of that development. Consider for example the implications of the
Soviet Union beginning to foster personal automobile transport in
the 1970's rather than in the 1920's.

CONCLUSION

In summary, it seems very difficult to differentiate
between the political-economic systems, and more specifically to
evaluate the soviet system, as to the long-term trends of spatial
economic development to be expected. Institutions, ideologies and
strategies vary over time, so that it is hard to produce a consistent
inductive definition of even the soviet system. Furthermore the
system comprises only one out of several groups of variables
affecting development, so that its connections with spatial change
over the long term are tenuous and shifting. On the other hand we
can analyse specific soviet projects in terms of the variables taken
into consideration and the institutional arrangements which help to
decide how they are taken into consideration. In a world where
basic goals and technologies of industrilising nations may be very
similar, it would seem worthwhile to pay much more attention than
hitherto to the effects of institutional variations on comparative
regional development. The distribution of decision-making with
respect to capital investment is one institutional characteristic of
great significance. The Soviet Union provides good illustrations of
this by being a rather extreme case of centralization, but the
corresponding institutions in Canada, the United States or any other
country are no less worthy of study for their importance in
regional development.

REFERENCES

1. Hamilton, F. E. I., "Models of Industrial Location," Models in Geography, Chorley, R. J. and P. Haggett (eds.) (London: Methuen, 1967), pp. 381-386 on Location Policy in the Socialist World.

2. Lavrishchev, A. N., Ekonomicheskaya Geograpfiya S.S.S.R. (Moscow: Ekonomika, 1965), pp. 3-4.

3. Grossman, G., Economic Systems (Englewood Cliffs: Prentice-Hall, 1967), p. 12; Buckingham, W. S., Jr., Theoretical Economic Systems: A Comparative Analysis (New York: Ronald Press, 1958), p. 90, as quoted by Grossman, op.cit., p. 3.

4. North, R. N., Transport and Economic Development in Western Siberia, unpublished Ph.D. dissertation, University of British Columbia (1968), pp. 437-445.

5. Principally, western Siberia and northern Kazakhstan were compared with the Canadian Prairie Provinces and adjacent states of the U.S.A., using two different regional boundaries; and the soviet and Canadian northlands were compared.

6. Bowden, E. V., "The Methodology of Long-Range (50-year) Projections of Regional Growth," Annals of Regional Science 3 (1969), pp. 76-86.

7. Chorley, R. J., "Geography and Analogue Theory," Annals of the Association of American Geographers 54 (1964), pp. 127-137.

8. Eckstein, A., "Economic Development and Political Change in Communist Systems," World Politics 22 (1970), p. 475.

9. Isard, W., et al., General Thoery: Social, Political, Economic and Regional, (Cambridge: M.I.T. Press, 1969), especially Chapter 3.

HAS THE PRAIRIE REGION SOLVED ITS
ECONOMIC PROBLEMS?

Brenton Barr
University of Alberta

INTRODUCTION

The 1930's were a turning point in the economic development of the Canadian prairies. Subsequently, domination by Winnipeg of the system of prairie cities has declined in face of the petroleum-based growth of Edmonton and Calgary.[1] The prairie agricultural labor force has been reduced by more than half, the region (assisted particularly by Alberta and Southern Saskatchewan) has become a significant producer of petroleum, the role of rail transportation has been reduced due to the advent of road, air and pipeline transportation, and the precambrian shield district has witnessed major increases in production of non-ferrous metals (Figure 1).[2] The prairie region has become an important supplier of fuel and raw materials to Canadian and American manufacturing regions. Many patterns of economic activity now suggest that the prairie economy is polarized around the Edmonton-Calgary corridor in the west, and the Winnipeg metropolitan region in the east.

The proportion of Canadians living in the prairie region has steadily declined from a peak of approximately one-quarter in 1931 to nearly one-sixth in 1966. A smaller percentage of the Canadian population is found in the region today than in 1911. The prairie employment structure has changed since the 1930's due to major technological improvements in farming practices which reduced the need for agricultural labor, and led to heavy migration of population from rural to urban areas.

111

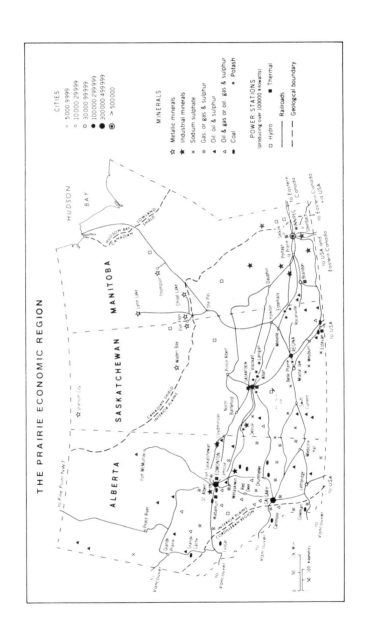

THE PRAIRIE ECONOMIC REGION

CITIES
○ 5000-9999
○ 10000-29999
○ 30000-99999
● 100000-299999
● 300000-499999
◉ > 500000

MINERALS
☆ Metallic minerals
★ Industrial minerals
✕ Sodium sulphate
⊗ Gas or gas & sulphur
▲ Oil & sulphur
△ Oil & gas or oil, gas & sulphur
● Coal
＊ Potash

POWER STATIONS
(producing over 100000 kilowatts)
□ Hydro   ■ Thermal

— Railroads
--- Geological boundary

The prairie region today appears to be characterized by economic stability brought about by a general reduction in the importance of agriculture to the regional economy. Economic change in the region, however, has not been a complete panacea for previous uncertainty and instability. Tentative assessment of prairie economic reorganization in this paper is based on answers to four questions. To what extent has industry replaced agriculture as the basis of the prairie economy? Does a slump in world demand for wheat still lead to serious economic dislocation within the region? Can a resource-extractive economy expect long-term economic growth and stability? Is the self-sustaining economic development of the past quarter century likely to continue for the next decade or will the region come to rely on governmental stabilization and incentive programs to provide the means for continued export-oriented economic growth?

RESOURCE EXTRACTION

Without economic development based on mineral discoveries, the prairie region by 1970 could have become a sparsely settled agricultural region primarily dependent for income on the cruel vagaries of an international grain market, and on the small Canadian market in which many prairie agricultural products compete with those from foreign and other domestic regions. Although markets for prairie agricultural commodities continue to fluctuate, thereby bringing hardships to many districts, the regional economy has undergone diversification away from a dependence on grain towards a dependence on other primary commodities.

It has been estimated that the largest export from Alberta following World War II "might well have been people" if petroleum had not been discovered.[3] Considerable emigration occurred from many eastern districts of the prairie region due to deficient employment opportunities. Eric Hanson has estimated that, without the petroleum industry, the population of the three prairie provinces of 3,381,000 in 1966 "would have been 1,676,000 less without the petroleum and mining industries. Of this additional population, the petroleum industry alone accounted for more than a million."[4]

Resource developments between 1946 and 1970 dis-
tinguish the past quarter century of prairie economic history from
preceding periods. Post-war growth in the North American consumption of increasingly distant supplies of liquid hydrocarbons,
non-ferrous metals, potash and wood pulp has encouraged integration of the prairie economy with the major market areas of Canada
and, particularly, of the United States.

DIVERSIFICATION OF EMPLOYMENT

Because the most important aspect of economic
reorganization since 1945 has been to provide alternate employment
in face of dwindling job opportunities in agriculture, selected
aspects of economic change are examined in this paper for their
possible significance to the diversification of employment, a
problem currently being researched by this author. A comprehensive review, however, of post-war changes in the prairie economy
and society has recently been provided by Richards.[5]

Despite an impressive rate of urbanization since 1941,
the percentage of people living in prairie urban areas is still
below the Canadian average of seventy-four per cent. At the
present time, approximately three-fifths of the prairie population
lives in urban areas, although the proportion of urban dwellers in
Saskatchewan remains below fifty per cent. The rural/urban
balance of Manitoba and Alberta approximates that of Canada as a
whole, suggesting thereby that, since World War II, a large
segment of both the prairie and the Canadian population has come
to be associated with a more diversified economic base. The
distribution of prairie population in urban places reflects the
relative importance of small agricultural and resource-extractive
towns and the dominant administrative, distributional and service
functions of the five largest regional centers.[6] Centers of inter-
mediate size with a strong secondary manufacturing base,
characteristic of southern Ontario and Quebec, are not yet significant in the system of prairie cities. A low density of population
in the region encourages major manufacturing enterprises to serve
the prairie market from plants located in central Canada, the
United States, or foreign countries. Furthermore, resource
development clearly has encouraged dispersion of settlement away
from the fertile agricultural districts, into the forested districts

114

frequently underlain both by rich mineral deposits and intermittent muskeg.

The relative importance of the tertiary sector in the aggregate prairie economy is identical to that of the Canadian and Ontario economies but the secondary sector is only half as important as in either Ontario or Canada as a whole (Figure 2). During the period 1951-1961, while the relative importance of secondary industry was declining in Ontario, the proportion in the prairie economy increased slightly. However, approximately thirty per cent of the prairie labor force in 1961 was employed in primary industry compared with only ten per cent in Ontario and a Canadian average of fourteen per cent.

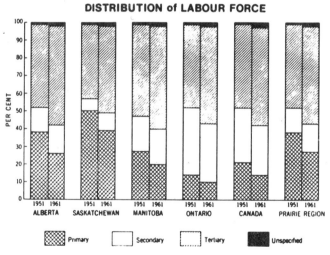

DISTRIBUTION of LABOUR FORCE

Source Census of Canada 1961 Bulletin SL-1 "Labour Force"

REGIONAL MARKETS

To the extent that heavy dependence on primary industry constitutes potential instability, then the prairie economy today is still potentially more unstable than that of either central Canada (represented by Ontario) or of Canada as a whole. Greater reliance on secondary and less on primary industry in Manitoba, characteristic of the average Canadian situation, reduced the economic impact in the recent past of a slump in international demand for prairie cereal grains. Manitoba's economy also has a wider resource base than that of the other two provinces. Operation L.I.F.T. (Low Inventories For Tomorrow) of the Canadian government in 1969-1970 was of very small consequence to Manitoba farmers, whereas it was of direct importance to those in Saskatchewan and numerous districts of Alberta. In a similar vein, recent self-imposed production quotas on Saskatchewan potash producers shows the danger of over-development and heavy reliance on one mineral as a panacea for economic growth. Despite the seemingly insatiable appetite of the United States for petroleum and natural gas, Alberta residents have viewed with apparent apprehension American decisions concerning oil import quotas, the pressure for which has come from American producers who seek to exclude cheaper Canadian oil from the domestic American markets. The ease with which oil and natural gas can be transported, the absence of a large regional market on the prairies, and a structure of freight rates which favors movement of raw materials instead of finished products, have reduced the impact which these fuels might have had on associated industrial development in the region. [7] Furthermore the increasing shortages in the supply of natural gas in the United States will probably increase the price which Canadians pay in the prairies as well, thereby further decreasing the attraction of an apparently cheap fuel. With America's worsening strategic position in the world and diminishing supplies of petroleum at home, the United States would probably not curtail the import of Canadian petroleum. Increasing demand alone in the United States appears to guarantee some access to American markets. However, the possibility of substitution of other fuels for oil and gas, or other sources of supply for prairie petroleum is of critical importance to the Saskatchewan and Alberta economies. [8] Recent development and exploration in regions outside the prairie provinces suggest that the boom of post-war exploration might be

116

over and that investment in leases and infrastructure may be far less important in the next decade. Consequently, if this is the kind of stability which resource extraction might bring, then an economy such as that of Manitoba or, indeed, Ontario, appears to be more stable.

Is the economic base of any region completely free from market uncertainty and unemployment? Diversity of the economic base and flexibility in the response of manufacturers to changes in market demand are of major importance to stability. However, a large proportion of the prairie manufacturing economy is oriented to regional markets and is, thereby, dependent on wealth generated by primary industry. Manufacturers of fertilizer for example, have recently seen markets decline due to adverse sales conditions for grains. Transportation costs tend to restrict sales of many products of this industry to markets in the prairie region and in adjacent American states. Successful Canadian sales to the USSR and China in the early 1960's led to prediction of ever-increasing export markets for prairie wheat. Fertilizer plants were established or expanded in anticipation of the need for greater yields by prairie farmers to meet heavy export obligations. However, many Canadian analysts failed to recognize that poor harvests in the USSR and China were followed by intensive government schemes to improve domestic agricultural production in those countries. With approximately two-fifths of the world's wheat surplus, Canadian producers are not heavy consumers of fertilizer and many plants are operating far below productive capacity.[9] The normal low rate of fertilizer application further decreased in 1970 due to a one-year program by the Federal Government to lower wheat inventories by promoting summer fallow and seeding of grass. Partial extension of this plan for three years is intended to encourage production of forage and growth of the prairie livestock industry. Prairie fertilizer manufacturers depend on international sales of grain and on a poorly-planned, unco-ordinated, and rather conservative prairie agricultural environment. Similarly, in many prairie districts, sales volumes of wholesalers and retailers depend directly on the ability of the agricultural sector to market grain and livestock. Businessmen in many districts of the prairie region will benefit from the strong international demand in the 1970-71 crop year for Canadian oilseeds and feed grains, and from the announcement by the Federal Government of measures to

117

encourage stabilization of income from grain sales and reduce
thereby the impact of fluctuations in world market prices.

Transportation costs are very important to fertilizer
and steel pipe producers due to the relatively low value of the
commodities in relation to their weight and bulk. Pipe mills are
located in Edmonton, Calgary, Camrose and Regina to manufacture
pipe for the transmission of oil and gas to American and Canadian
markets. Full production at these mills depends upon continuous
expansion of the prairie transmission networks and a steady flow
of orders for pipe. The last discovery of a major oil field in
Alberta occurred in 1966. Prairie pipe manufacturers expect that
a large proportion of their production in the 1970's will be used in
the construction of a major oil and gas transmission line from the
Arctic via the Mackenzie Valley to American markets. Pipe manufacturers are subject to many forces from outside the prairie region
such as demand for petroleum and gas, prices of foreign petroleum
discovery of new petroleum deposits, determination of export
policies by Federal and Provincial Governments, and the actions of
integrated steel companies located outside the region. The long
delay in 1970 of approval of major exports of natural gas by the
Canadian National Energy Board caused severe disruption in production of pipe by at least one major prairie pipe manufacturer. In
addition, with only one prairie integrated steel-pipe operation,
most pipe manufacturers purchase steel outside the region from
producers who also manufacture pipe in direct competition with
prairie mills.

In addition to cereal grains, potash, crude oil, and
natural gas, the prairie region is an exporter of sulphur, nickel,
copper, uranium, zinc, sodium sulphate, wood pulp and coal.
Most of the final manufacturing and consumption of these commodities is carried out in other regions. Whether agricultural or
industrial, the basic commodities produced in the prairie region
continue to be exported in unprocessed form. Since these industria
commodities are consumed by industry in other regions, the implication is that they could be used to support manufacturing establish
ments in the prairie region.

CONCLUSIONS

Post-war economic growth through infusion of foreign capital into resource development has reduced the dependence of much of the labor force on agriculture by increasing the importance of other sectors of the economy. The chief benefit to many parts of the region has been direct and associated employment. Although the employment structure is now more diversified than prior to World War II, production of most prairie commodities continues to depend on extraregional demand.

The prairie region is similar to many world regions in that domestic governments cannot guarantee stability in the price of export commodities. Recent prairie developments related to potash, coal, tar sand, wood pulp, and agricultural processing, however, suggest that the Federal and Provincial Governments will play an increasingly strong role, through a variety of financial incentives, in assisting individual producers to increase their ability to offer primary commodities at competitive prices in world markets.

The current function of the prairie economy -- to supply raw materials to manufacturing regions -- will probably continue until such time as natural population increase provides sufficient markets to support major secondary manufacturing establishments in the region.

REFERENCES

1. Changes in freight rate structures, removal of special rail
        privileges, and strengthened regional economies
        enabled other prairie centers (Regina, Saskatoon,
        Edmonton and Calgary) to become relatively independer
        of Winnipeg after 1914. Many activities which were
        originally localized in Winnipeg became decentralized
        in the prairie region. Support for this argument is
        provided by Karl Lenz, 'Large Urban Places in the
        Prairie Provinces -- Their Development and Location,
        in Gentilcore, R.L. (ed.), Canada's Changing
        Geography (Scarborough, Ont.: Prentice-Hall, 1967),
        p. 204.

2. Population and employment data for various years have been
        obtained from The Census of Canada, Dominion Burea
        of Statistics, Ottawa.

3. Gray, Earle, Impact of Oil (Toronto: Ryerson Press/Maclean
        Hunter Ltd., 1969), p. 98.

4. Quoted in Gray, op. cit., p. 99.

5. Richards, J. H. "The Prairie Region," in Warkentin, J. (ed.)
        Canada, A Geographical Interpretation (Toronto:
        Methuen, 1968), pp. 396-437.

6. The historical growth of these centers is assessed in Lenz,
        op. cit.

7. Some manufacturers of petrochemicals and other products,
        such as ammonia, who located near gas fields in centr.
        Alberta in the early 1950's prior to construction of
        export natural gas pipelines have subsequently found
        that the cost of distributing finished products to easter:
        markets has increased faster than the cost of assemb-
        ling natural gas at such markets. For those prairie
        manufacturers whose major markets are located in

central Canada and abroad, a raw-material oriented
location can be a serious disadvantage.

8. The value of petroleum production (natural gas, natural gas
by-products, and crude oil) in the prairie region was
$1.2 billion in 1968. Manitoba accounted for 1.3%,
Saskatchewan for 18.7%, and Alberta for 80%. In 1968,
production of petroleum comprised 7.5% of provincial
mineral production in Manitoba, 60% in Saskatchewan,
and 88% in Alberta. A Summary of the Economic
Conditions in the Provinces of British Columbia,
Alberta, Saskatchewan, and Manitoba. Alberta Bureau
of Statistics, Department of Industry and Tourism,
Government of Alberta, 1969.

9. Canada accounted for approximately 40% of the main world
exporters' carry-over of wheat in 1970. The United
States accounted for approximately 36%. IFAP NEWS,
20, No. 1 (January, 1971), p. 2.

SMALL INDUSTRIES IN ASIAN COUNTRIES:
THE HONG KING EXAMPLE[1]

Chuen Yan Lai
University of Victoria

INTRODUCTION

In recent years, developing nations are paying more attention to the study of small industries for socio-economic reasons, and examining their development with respect to urban growth and planning problems. Small industries play an important role in national economic progress because they manufacture goods for local consumption as well as for export. In addition they provide industrial employment, thereby helping to solve problems created by rural or urban unemployment. However, in some countries, small manufacturing units within urban centres have created problems of physical planning. A large number of them are squatters, and are housed in flimsy structures in areas which have no urban amenities and facilities for industry. In some cases, small manufacturing units have infiltrated into the rural areas, and ruined the environment of the countryside. This paper examines some aspects of small industries in Hong Kong, hoping that the observations of this case study may provide valuable information for other developing countries.

DEFINITION

In discussing small manufacturing units, a problem of definition immediately arises. As many developing countries are at different stages of industrial development, they have different criteria to define their small industries. The number of employees, capital investment, power equipment and economic structure are commonly used to define small industries. Small

123

industries in Indonesia, for example, include all the manufacturing establishments with less than ten full-time workers and not using machinery. In some Middle-East countries such as Israel, Turkey and Egypt, small industries are also referred to as those establishments employing less than ten persons. However, some countries regard the number of employees as a misleading criterion for small industries, because a unit employing 20 persons may have a substantial capital investment which may include the value of land, building and other fixed assets. India, for example, defines small industries as those establishments possessing no more than Rs. 1,000,000 of capital (about U.S. $200,000).[2] In Ceylon, small industries are those using power, but possessing no more than Rs. 200,000 (U.S. $40,000), of capital investment in machinery and equipment. The Working Party on Cottage and Small Scale Industries of the ESCAFE attempted in 1952 to standardize terminology by suggesting that cottage industry should be defined as one which is carried on wholly or primarily with the help of members of the family, either as a whole or as part-time occupation. A small-scale industry is then one which is operated mainly with hired labour, usually not exceeding 50 workers in any establishment or unit not using any motive power in any operation, or up to 20 workers in an establishment or unit using such power.

As there are no internationally recognized criteria to define small industries, Asian countries such as Indonesia, Burma, Pakistan and the Philippines, tend to use the ECAFE's definition with slight amendments to suit local conditions. Staley and Morse regard the number of employees as the "least objectionable" of the generally available measures in classifying the size of industrial establishments, and they defined small industry as all manufacturing carried on in establishments with fewer than 100 employees, but they also emphasized that the functional differences were more important in distinguishing small industries from other forms of manufacturing.[4]

There is no official definition for small industries in Hong Kong. The Loans for Small Industry Committee, set up in 1968 by the Trade and Industry Advisory Board, made no attempt to define small scale industry. They thought that "any definition established earlier might well have reduced the scope of the survey work done by the Commerce and Industry Department, denied use

information to the Committee."[5] Nevertheless, the Committee
tentatively suggested that a small-scale factory should be "one
which directly employs not more than 200 workers and has total
proprietors funds of not more than HK$600,000 (about U.S.
$100,000)," but the Committee also suggested that this definition
should be revised after more information has been collected on
small industries.[6] In view of these circumstances, the definition
of small industry used in this paper is very arbitrary. The paper
deals with manufacturing units employing less than 100 workers.
The common characteristics of these small units are one-man
management, shortage of working space and capital, weak bargain-
ing power for prices of supplies and products, and quasi-
independence on subcontract work from larger firms.

THE ECONOMIC ROLE OF SMALL INDUSTRIES

Small manufacturing units play an important role in the
industrial structure of Hong Kong both in terms of numbers of
employees and in terms of exports. The official statistics show
that between March 1950 and March 1970, the number of industrial
undertakings rose from 1,525 to 15,285. Of the latter, a total of
13,466 (or 88.10%) employed less than 100 workers, and a total of
7,121 (or 46.59%) employed fewer than 10 workers.[7] Of the
568,787 industrial employees in March 1970, nearly 40 per cent
worked in small units. These industrial undertakings did not
include those which were not registered with or recorded by the
Labour Department.[8] The official data on the number of industrial
employees also exclude outworkers or those employed in very small
industrial concerns and home industries.[9] Should these workers
be included in the official statistics, the number of employees
engaged in small industries would be much greater. Small
industries in Hong Kong provide, therefore, many employment
opportunities for both the urban and rural residents. It was
estimated in 1967 that the livelihood of some 145,000 families
depended on small scale factories,[10] and small scale factories
manufactured in 1968 nearly 60 per cent by value of the domestic
products exported to Britain.[11] In addition, small units carry out
subcontract work for larger manufacturing firms, and perform
jobs which might have been done in one portion of a large factory.
This kind of contribution to manufacturing is very often not
revealed in official statistics.

In spite of their indispensable contributions to the economic growth of Hong Kong, small industries have also create many problems for the physical planning of Hong Kong, because of their chaotic spatial pattern in many densely populated residentia districts and squatter areas. These problems may be illustrated by the proliferation of small units in three selected areas within the twin cities of Victoria and Kowloon.

SMALL INDUSTRIES IN THREE SAMPLE AREAS

Tai Kok Tsui is a mixed residential-commercial-industrial district on the north-western part of Kowloon. A surve in 1962 revealed that within a small area of about 130 acres in the district, there were no less than 377 industrial undertakings employing about 9,250 workers.[12] Most of the establishments employed less than 100 workers, and the average number of workers was about 24 per unit. In spite of their small scale in terms of employment, they manufactured a great variety of commodities: textile goods, rubber footwear, glassware, metal trays, pressure stoves, hurricane lamps and other articles. Most of these small factories were located on the ground floor as well as on upper floors of permanent buildings, which were basic ally residential blocks. Many were housed in wooden huts in an area where there were no paved streets and no storage facilities. Heaps of raw materials and finished products lay in open storage between the huts and on the streets. The area is a classic example of unplanned industrial development in Hong Kong.

The chaotic industrial pattern is repeated in the Ngau Tau Kok district which lies on the north-eastern part of Kowloon. A sample survey of a part of the district in 1965 revealed that within an area of less than seven acres, 76 industrial undertakin were engaged in great variety of industries.[13] The most importa groups of enterprises were foundries, rolling mills and metal workshops. Most of these industrial units were housed in tempo ary structures which were set so closely together that they const tuted a serious fire hazard. After the area was cleared in 1965, only about half of the industrial units in the Ngau Tau Kok area were re-located in resettlement factories provided by the government.[14]

The third sample area is Western District on Hong Kong Island which is a typical example of a run-down residential district characterized by many dilapidated buildings, mixed land uses and inadequate urban amenities. An area of about 14 acres within the District was studied in the summer of 1970. The survey revealed that of 115 small manufacturing units employing nearly 1,000 workers, about 30% were not required by regulation to be registered with or recorded by the Labour Department.[15] About 50% of these units were tiny artisan workshops, employing less than five workers each. These units are housed in the basement or on the ground floor or upper floors of old buildings. In some cases, they occupy the front part of a floor while the rear part is used for residential purposes. Limited by the small space inside the workshop, the manufacturer tends to use the pavements as a storing place for crates, boxes and bags of material supplies and finished products. Terraces, lanes, and alleys where many of these small units are located are very often littered with piles of debris and refuse. The entire area has deteriorated so badly that it can only be rehabilitated by a comprehensive programme of urban renewal.

RELOCATION POLICY FOR SMALL INDUSTRIES

The three areas described above present a patchwork quilt of small manufacturing units, which presents many problems for urban re-development. The present relocation policy concerning small industries is but a by-product of other policies, notably those concerning the resettlement of squatters, which has led to the construction of multi-storey resettlement factory blocks. According to this policy, small factories which are found in squatter areas or in areas under annual Crown land permits are eligible for resettlement when these areas are cleared for permanent development. In 1969, there were 22 resettlement highrise factory blocks, most of which are situated in or near existing resettlement estates.[16] This relocation programme is of limited value, for a number of reasons. Firstly, the resettlement policy is to relocate factories from squatter areas, therefore the small factories housed in blighted residential areas within the urban centers are not qualified for resettlement. Secondly, not all the factories in the squatter areas are eligible for resettlement. For example, several important categories of such industries as foundries, rolling mills, sawmills, food factories, leather factories and others are excluded from the factory resettlement blocks. These factories can be resettled only if the manufacturers are willing to change their trades. Warehouses and garages which are classified as non-industrial, and factories which occupy a space greater than 5,000 square feet, are again not eligible for resettlement. Thirdly, the locations of these resettlement factory blocks are not decided according to the small factories requirements concerning area, community, and site. It is evident that the government should formulate a sound policy for the relocation of the small industries from the squatter areas as well as from the blighted residential areas. The Loans for Small Industry Committee, which was formed to study small industries in Hong Kong, should, therefore, recommend to the Government a financial assistance programme for relocation of all small industries within the urban areas of Hong Kong.

CONCLUSION

One of the main problems of urbanization in developing countries is that city growth far exceeds economic development, and especially industrialization progress. This results in urban unemployment, under-employment and urban poverty. The promotion and development of small industries is, therefore, essential to provide urban employment opportunities, and can be seen as a method of overcoming some obstacles to industrialization in developing countries, particularly the obstacles of capital shortage, poor quality of industrial labour and narrow market opportunities. In the final analysis, it is not only necessary to recognize the economic importance of small industries in developing countries, but also essential to give attention to planning problems associated with these small industries. Planning of new industrial towns and urban renewal is a widespread movement, not only in Western nations, but also in many Asian countries such as Singapore, South Korea, and Hong Kong. As a complementary measure to urban renewal and planning of new towns, it is important to study the plant site requirements of small manufacturing firms in order to formulate a rational location policy for small industries.

128

REFERENCES

1. This study is based mainly on the author's previous field work and partly on his field study in 1970 under a research grant from Canada Council.

2. Economic Survey of Asia and the Far East, 1958, (Bangkok, United Nations, 1959), p. 100.

3. Rao, R. V. Cottage and Small Scale Industries and Planned Economy (Delhi: Sterling Publishers, 1967), p. 18.

4. Staley, E. and Morse, R. Modern Small Industry for Developing Countries (New York: McGraw-Hill Book Co., 1965), pp. 14-15.

5. Report of the Loans for Small Industry Committee to the Trade and Industry Advisory Board, Hong Kong, 1970, p. 6 (unpublished).

6. Ibid.

7. Unpublished data, Labour Department, Hong Kong Government.

8. The Labour Department only registers those industrial undertakings employing more than twenty persons, or those employing less than twenty persons but using power-driven machinery, coal gas, gasoline or any inflammable or dangerous liquid. It also keeps a record of those with fifteen or nineteen workers where women and young persons are employed, and where manufacturing processes involve health or safety hazards.

9. Hong Kong Government, Commissioner of Labour, Annual Departmental Report, 1960-1961 (Hong Kong, 1961), p. 10.

10. The result of the Household Expenditure Survey in 1963-

1964, quoted by Law, Louis T. P. 'Significance of
Small-scale Factories in Hong Kong," Hong Kong
Productivity News, Vol. 2, No. 8, (1959), p. 6.

11. Report of the Loans for Small Industry Committee, op. cit.
p. 7.

12. Dwyer, D. J. and Lai, C. Y. The Small Industrial Unit in
Hong Kong: Patterns and Policies (University of
Hull, Occasional Papers in Geography No. 6, 1967),
p. 42.

13. Ibid., p. 60.

14. Ibid., p. 63.

15. Personal interview in summer 1970.

16. Hong Kong Annual Report, 1969, (Hong Kong Government,
1969), p. 124.

ABSTRACTS OF PAPERS

TITLES OF PAPERS NOT INCLUDED IN THIS

VOLUME

ABSTRACTS

        Abstracts of papers presented at the annual meeting of
the Western Division of the Canadian Association of Geographers,
University of British Columbia, March 6th, 1971, but not printed
in this volume.

J. Cromwell (Selkirk College): SOCIAL SPACE IN THE RURAL-
        URBAN FRINGE

        The concept of social space includes within it an
objective element of the observable spatial framework in which
people live and a subjective element of their perception of that
space. By using the procedures of Chapin for measuring househol
activity systems to establish an objective social space, and the
image testing procedures of Lynch to establish a subjective social
space, an attempt has been made to study the differing concepts of
social space of long-term residents and recent migrants to a
rural-urban fringe area of Vancouver, B. C.

D. W. Couch (Cariboo College): SPATIAL FACTORS IN
        COMMUNITY DEVELOPMENT IN BRITISH COLUMBIA

        During the past seven years British Columbia has
experienced very rapid growth in the development of public
community colleges. Eight such colleges are now operating -- the
first opened in 1965. These institutions have been established to
meet two primary needs: a more comprehensive system of post-
secondary education, and to provide students throughout the
province with equal opportunities for obtaining a post-secondary
education. Or, as John B. Macdonald described it ". . . diversification of opportunity, both in respect to the kinds of educational
experience available and the places where it can be obtained."

        This paper will consider enrollments in the British

132

Columbia post-secondary institutions, and indicate to what extent the accessibility to higher education objective is being met. The role of spatial factors will be outlined and their low priority in college development discussed.

E. D. Lubitz (University of Calgary): DEVELOPMENT OF A
MODEL FOR RESERVOIR DELTA VOLUME
ESTIMATION

A general model in the form $W_r = 0.15hR$ is developed using the following parameters: the amount of sediment per unit width (Wr) below the high water line, the vertical height of the delta foreset beds (h), the depth of the top of the foreset beds at the high water mark and the total length of reservoir induced sedimentation (R) which is derived from the distance to the foreset beds from the high water mark divided by a constant 0.3. The constant is obtained from a ratio between the initial bed slope and the subsequent bed slope after integration along the length of the delta. The model was applied to the Glenmore Reservoir, Calgary, Alberta, where estimates of the delta volume were within six per cent of those determined in 1967.

John Marsh (University of Calgary): IDEAS FOR UNDER-
GRADUATE FIELD STUDY

This paper aims to emphasize the value of, and the exciting possibilities for, undergraduate field study in geography, and is largely based on experience gained through the provision of an experimental field study programme for introductory geography students at the University of Calgary.

Two basic types of field study are identified and the value of these activities considered. Means to overcome the traditional problems of numbers, cost and instruction are suggested. Various original types of field trip are discussed and the nature and success of the programme at Calgary reviewed.

The need for field study centres, at home and abroad, for undergraduates and high school students, is discussed. Suggestions for more inventive travel-study programmes, using ships, trains, planes, and the current hitch-hiking vogue, are offered.

133

Willis B. Merriam (Washington State University): SOME ASPECTS
OF CONSERVATION AND ENVIRONMENTAL QUALITY
AWARENESS IN THE PACIFIC NORTHWEST

As a participating member of perhaps the first course
in Conservation of Natural Resources taught in a Geography
Department in the Pacific Northwest -- University of Washington,
1931 -- I am uniquely able to observe and comment upon numerous
changes in public attitudes that have evolved since the days of
indifference, skepticism or open hostility toward teaching in this
field, to the current, though as yet inadequate efforts to place
environmental quality control on a practical basis, scientifically
sound and acceptable to both the industrial and the concerned
social sides of our economy.

P. Murphy (University of Victoria) and R. Golledge (Ohio State
University): THE POSITION OF ATTITUDE
THEORY AND RESEARCH AS A POTENTIAL
VARIABLE IN URBAN GEOGRAPHY RESEARCH

The paper notes the increased use of behavioural
concepts that has taken place in urban geography and suggests that
a major weakness in past research has been the inability to
adequately isolate and measure some of the intangible forces that
are considered to be acting upon the spatial decisions and patterns
within the urban area. It is proposed that a possible solution to
the problem may exist in the utilization of certain attitude theories
and measurements which have been developed in the field of social
psychology. The applicability of the attitude concept to urban
geography problems is discussed and some measurement techniques are reviewed within the same context. The paper concludes
that with certain behavioural forces so defined and measured the
urban geographer is better able to construct comprehensive models
of spatial behaviour.

June M. Ryder and Michael Church (University of British
Columbia): PARAGLACIAL SEDIMENTATION

Glaciation is schematically considered as a perturba-
tion of "normal" fluvial conditions. Following deglacerization,
drift deposits are unstable in the succeeding fluvial environment,

resulting in heightened sediment movement that continues as long as drift material remains easily accessible for fluvial erosion and transpo rtation. During this "paraglacial" period, sediment yield bears no relationship to concurrent primary production of weathered debris.

Examples of paraglacial denudation and sedimentation are reported from two contrasting areas. Post-glacial valley alluvial deposits are widespread in central Baffin Island where rapid sedimentation continues today. Estimated denudation rates are order-of-magnitude higher than in comparable unperturbed areas. In south central British Columbia, rapid sedimentation during the paraglacial period contrasts sharply with present day conditions.

M. J. Scarlett (University of Calgary): URBAN TRAVEL, THE
           COMPUTER AND CYBERNETICS

Among the more important aspects of the problem of movement within cities is that of temporal and spatial disequilibria. It is suggested that the usual diagnosis of the problem leads to solutions which are not optimal. Evidence is offered from an empirical study of traffic in the Greater Montreal area which suggests that a neglected study concerns the re-distribution of flows over existing roads. Such a re-distribution would imply moving to an aggregate travel time minimization objective. Individual decision making is however based on personal benefit, rather than the public good. A cybernetic approach is thus proposed to reconcile these objectives. Some implications are briefly noted.

Colin Wood (University of Victoria): CHARACTERISTICS OF
           SEARCHING BY URBAN DECISION MAKERS

Searching the environment is an important part of the learning process, common to much of man's activities. The consumer "shops around" comparing prices or looking for the article desired. The company explores resource areas, potential markets or sites for new plant locations. The spatial characteristics of this process and the operating rules involved are hypothesized in several recent studies. However, there is still

135

a real need to expand empirical knowledge of the process. In this
paper the spatial characteristics of searching by municipalities
during the evaluation of innovations is described and simple
relationships with distance and identify preference hypothesized.

TITLES

The following papers were also presented at the
meeting:

F. Leversedge (University of Victoria): THE AUTARKIC
PRINCIPLE IN SOVIET ECONOMIC DEVELOPMENT

G. Young (Washington State University): THE ECOLOGICAL
APPROACH IN CONTEMPORARY GEOGRAPHY

R. Brown and J. Horsman (Simon Fraser University): PLACE T
PLACE VARIATIONS IN RETAIL GROCERY PRICES
IN VANCOUVER

A. McPherson (Simon Fraser University): MARGINAL MAN AND
GEOGRAPHICAL PERSPECTIVE

N. D. Cherukapallee (University of British Columbia): GROWTH
POLE CONCEPT: AN INDIAN APPLICATION

B.C. GEOGRAPHICAL SERIES

BOX 4248, VANCOUVER 9, CANADA

B. C. Geographical Series is published by Tantalus Research Limited on a pro re nata basis.

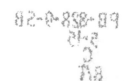